WAYS OF KNOWING

The Reality Club

John Brockman
Editor

PRENTICE
HALL
PRESS

New York   London   Toronto   Sydney   Tokyo   Singapore

Portions of this book were originally published as *The Reality Club*
by Lynx Books, a division of Lynx Communications, Inc.

PRENTICE HALL PRESS
15 Columbus Circle
New York, NY 10023

Copyright © 1988, 1991, by John Brockman Associates, Inc.

Library of Congress Cataloging-in-Publication Data

Ways of knowing / John Brockman, editor.
p.   cm. — (The Reality Club ; 3)
Includes bibliographical references.
ISBN 0-13-517236-5
1. Philosophy. 2. Reality. 3. Life. I. Brockman, John, 1941–
II. Series: Reality Club (Series) ; 3.
B73.W38   1991
100—dc20   90-7797
CIP

Designed by Irving Perkins Associates

Manufactured in the United States of America

10 9 8 7 6 5 4 3 2 1

First Edition

Contents

Contents

Artificial Life: A Conversation with Chris Langton and Doyne Farmer

INTERVIEWED BY JOHN BROCKMAN

I think it's true to say that, whether it happens in the next ten or a hundred or a thousand years, we're at the stage where it has become possible to create living things that are connected to us not so much by material as by information. In geological time, we're literally at the end of one era of evolution and at the beginning of another.

Chris Langton and Doyne Farmer are at the forefront of people defining the new field of Artificial Life. They divide their time between Los Alamos and The Santa Fe Institute. They are similar in that they are both lean longhairs, about the same age (Langton forty, Farmer thirty-seven), and are actively pursuing a vision of tackling the issue of biological complexity by developing and understanding emergent beings. I admire their intellectual hunger and desire.

I videotaped the following interview during lunch in a crowded and noisy New Mexican restaurant on Canyon Road in Santa Fe, much to the amusement of our waitress, the consternation of some diners (who were annoyed by the exuberant nature of Langton and Farmer), and the excitement of other diners (who believed they were watching the taping of a segment of "Lifestyles of the Rich and Famous").

FARMER: The questions we are asking ourselves are: What are adaptive systems? What makes them tick? Why are they different from other things? As you begin asking these questions you find yourself rolling back to even more basic questions such as: What is life? Why is life really different from something that isn't alive?

BROCKMAN: Is that latter question an important question or is it just a way of framing your work on adaptive systems?

FARMER: Both. You have to take an angle on something and decide what attitude you are going to have. I approach these questions as a physicist, and most of physics is focused on properties of inanimate matter and on movements of matter and structure of matter. But all the questions in physics are framed from a very reductionist point of view. If you want to understand how matter organizes itself, how information gets moved around between structures that contain matter, then you are forced to ask very different kinds of questions than the more reductionist kind that traditionally have been asked. The big difficulty has been that these different kinds of questions are harder to ask, and may require new points of view than those of the traditional approaches that have been taken.

Physics as a science has largely been defined by what's tractable and simple, what can actually be done. Physicists ferret out simple situations and then try to exploit that simplicity to make much stronger statements about nature than could possibly be made through other means. What we are thrashing around with now is, where are those simple problems in which you can use something like a hydrogen atom as a handle to delve into these questions and say something more definite about them? But we are still in the groping stage because, first of all, these questions are hard and, second, we haven't gone very far toward addressing them as we haven't had the tools for long, which we had needed to really address them.

BROCKMAN: Where is the new framework you are developing going to take you? What do you hope to discover or find out?

LANGTON: For a long time, science has been dealing with systems by coming up with models and explanations for things that were simpler than the systems themselves. In order to do that scientists have had to pick certain things in nature that were susceptible to being explained with simple models. The kinds of questions that we're asking are about those things in nature that, in some sense, may be their own simplest descriptions. So I think science is up against a new kind of problem: What is the scientist's role in trying to understand something for which he's probably not going to be able to come up with a much simpler description?

FARMER: You don't try to describe the whole thing. You try to extract those properties that are less than the whole yet, nonetheless, give you some idea about what makes the thing tick.

The small disagreement with what you said comes from the thought that, even with these adaptive systems, they may be their own simplest description, if you want to understand every little detail about them, but I believe their salient parts (and this is really just a belief) can be gotten after abstractions that are simpler than those things themselves. At the same time, of course, there may be irreducible levels of complexity in these descriptions that we can't dive past.

LANGTON: Those irreducible complexities are what I'm talking about. The whole notion of Artificial Life is trying to abstract the relevant details of living things from the, probably irrelevant, details of the particular material in which life happened to emerge on the planet earth. So the goal is to abstract what it is to be alive from the material.

We would like to get a better understanding of what life is for many different reasons and it's hard to do so by studying the life that we know, because we just have this one example.

BROCKMAN: What can you compare it to?

LANGTON: Ah, there's a loaded question. You can think of a computer in two ways: You can think of a computer as something that runs a program and calculates a number, or you can think of a computer as a kind of logical universe, a digital universe that you can make behave in many different ways. We believe we can put into computers sufficiently complex universes able to support processes that, with respect to that universe, would have to be considered alive. They would behave in that universe the way living things do in this universe but they wouldn't be made out of the same stuff.

To do this raises a lot of possibilities. One is, if we can accept that they are alive, the empirical base upon which we are going to be able to build general theories of life is broadened. As it stands, it is very difficult to build general theories of life based on theoretical biology. We can't make statements about what life would be like anywhere else in the universe; we can only talk about what we know here.

Also, it raises the awesome possibility that we are going to be participating in creating the next living things in the universe. If we can actually bring life into that which is not part of our ancestral tree, if we are able to abstract the necessary information and dynamical structure from the material that has been informed by this structure and implement it in some other stuff, an enormous number of possibilities and questions are raised.

BROCKMAN: What might be an example of a life form that gets created?

LANGTON: I think there's a whole spectrum of possibilities, if we can get things going within computers—that is, within environments within computers that are effectively alive and using evolutionary principles to get things to adapt within these environments.

BROCKMAN: For example?

LANGTON: John Holland's classifier systems, or other systems that use genetic principles in order to search a large problem space to help find optimal solutions or to help find better solutions than the ones we know. They are using principles imported from biology, those of mutation and genetic recombination—programs that are represented in such a way that most of the operations we do to them will result in viable programs.

You take populations of these programs and let them work on their environment, which is the problem, and the better ones reproduce sexually, in some sense. They have crossover among themselves, and create new variants on the basis of a population of programs that did pretty well already. So you are using the principles of variation and natural selection within a computer and, although you might not call them organisms, they are in fact evolving. Another example that comes close to being alive is computer viruses, which satisfy a lot of the criteria for living things.

BROCKMAN: They are rapidly becoming illegal.

LANGTON: They are rapidly proliferating.

BROCKMAN: Maybe the pro-life people will get into it. . . .

FARMER: Except we don't have rights for real viruses, or bacteria or chickens for that matter. Somehow, we single ourselves out to have this right to life. I had an argument with a vegetarian friend whom I told if you're really a vegetarian you should never turn off your computer! It's just a matter of where you draw the cutoff on the hierarchy and whether you believe in the hierarchy.

BROCKMAN: Can you give me specific examples of life forms that you are creating?

FARMER: That question raises the issue of the definition of the word *life*. Lifeness should perhaps be thought of as a continuous property. To me, a machine is a little more alive than a rock and probably less alive than a virus, which is less alive than a bacteria, which is probably less alive than I am. (Of course I put myself up at the top.)

But nature can throw Avogadro's numbers of computers at something because its got zillions of molecules, all of which act like independent parallel processors. We can't really do that. We don't have that kind of computing power at our disposal, so we are forced to make these abstractions where we take an aspect of something out and build a little model around it that does what the original does, and so we have models of living things. But one of the thorny questions here is, When does a model of a living thing turn into a living thing? Because if the model starts incorporating enough of the properties of a living thing then, at a certain point, maybe it becomes alive.

LANGTON: Many people have a problem with such a basic distinction and will say that no matter how like the real thing the model is it can never have attributed to it a life as if it were a living thing. It's a fundamental difference. Basically we sit on the other side of that fence. We think that if it smells like a dog and barks like a dog and eats like a dog, you might as well call it a dog. Whether or not it's made out of the same stuff is irrelevant.

BROCKMAN: I imagine you have people who are detractors.

LANGTON: Surprisingly enough, I'm getting some fairly severe criticism, not for Artificial Life per se but for being a computationalist in Artificial Life.

FARMER: I got called a mechanist by Rupert Sheldrake. "You mechanist!!!," he said.

BROCKMAN: Can I call my ten-year-old son, Max, with his Nintendo "Game Boy," a computationalist?

LANGTON: It depends on whether he believes that what's in the Nintendo game could actually have its own kinds of properties and be a thing in and of itself, have its own kind of existence. It is the same kind of criticism that's being leveled against Artificial Intelligence: A computer could never be "conscious." The people who are throwing barbs are people who have been in systems science.

FARMER: Philosophers, too, such as John Searle. To me this is a silly debate. The biggest piece of ammunition Searle has is that the Artificial Intelligence guys haven't come up with anything intelligent. If they had something that could pass the Turing test or could do things that at least appear to be intelligent, they would have something to go back at him with. Eventually I think they will, but it's just going to take longer than they originally stated. They made the mistake in 1950 of saying that they could accomplish this in ten to twenty years.

BROCKMAN: How does your work intersect with AI?

FARMER: Living systems are simpler than intelligent systems. Life can be achieved by a bacteria or maybe even a virus, and it is clearly a much simpler thing than the human brain. Part of the motive for studying Artificial Life instead of Artificial Intelligence is to tackle some easier problems first, rather than jump directly to intelligence. Let's see if we can even grasp the basic principles that keep a bacteria going. But there are a lot of commonalities between A-life and AI. The whole notion of adaptation and evolution clearly underlies both those systems, and many of the organizational principles behind intelligence and behind life are similar. Intelligence sprang out of life. So there are a lot of common questions, common threads, and common brick walls.

LANGTON: I find it hard to draw a dividing line between them as well. Starting with intelligence, starting with a study of systems that determine their own behavior due to information structures they contain inside themselves, the AI people picked the most complex example in that group, intelligent things, and were misled by the fact that it is easy to get computers to do things that human beings consider hard. And so they met with a lot of initial success at what turned out to be not very difficult problems.

Richard Dawkins gives a nice example: If you take a dead bird and throw it into the air, it traces out a beautiful parabola in obeyance to simple physical forces. However, if you throw a live bird into the air, although it is influenced by gravitational forces, it's trajectory is largely determined by itself using information processing going on in the bird. So my aim is to understand how, in a universe dominated by energy, there came to be processes dominated by information systems that determine their own behavior far removed from basic physical forces acting upon them.

It is going to be hard to understand these things by starting with intelligence. I think that we're going to learn some basic things about intelligence by studying other things, such as bacteria, that exhibit their own self-determining behavior. Both living things and intelligent things behave and determine their own behavior, and so it's the study of these behaving systems that I think we're all after.

BROCKMAN: Where do you see your A-life work leading in the next five years?

FARMER: One goal that I hope we can accomplish in the next five years is to come up with some examples of things we can call Artificial Life without having to cross our fingers and make a lot of exceptions and provisos. That would give us the platform to do the experiments we need to do to make a theory. This is analogous to the development of thermodynamics and statistical mechanics in the last century. We need a Joule to get in there and find a set of simple experiments that have quantitative results.

BROCKMAN: What's that experiment going to be, if you had to guess?

LANGTON: After digesting everything presented at the first Artificial Life Workshop, we realized there was a kind of fundamental architecture underlying most of the better models that we saw. In hindsight, it's lots of simple things interacting with one another to do something complicated collectively. Our goal at the moment is to try to build a software simulation package on the Connection Machine that we have at Los Alamos. It's going to take that kind of machine because, as Doyne mentioned, the kind of computational power that nature has thrown at the simplest living thing is far in excess of what we have. Technologies such as the Connection Machine are only beginning to bring us closer to the kinds of complexity of interaction of simple programs.

BROCKMAN: Is the Connection Machine in itself nature working?

LANGTON: It's a lot closer to the way nature works.

BROCKMAN: Is the existence of the tool, and what the tool does, that which becomes real in the sense that without the tool, without the measurement, you don't have anything?

FARMER: The Connection Machine is a physical system that's also designed to simulate other physical systems. You can use it in either mode. You can think of a computer as just a device for calculating the solution to a problem, or you can think of it as a universe. You can view it as an artificial universe into which you can insert artificial laws of physics and chemistry, push the start button and then see what these artificial chemistries and physics give rise to. So we're very much working with this artificial universe approach in trying to understand nature.

Once we begin to have interesting things going on inside of artificial universes, then we can begin to use these artificial universes to try to get at basic questions; for instance, your question about the Connection Machine. One, is there a threshold of complexity that we have to reach in order for something to behave as though it were alive? It is not clear to me whether the Connection Machine is powerful enough to reach such a threshold of complexity. There seem to be such thresholds in a lot of systems. For instance, the machine that replicates ourselves, this templating, protein, DNA machine, seems to have a minimum complexity threshold below which it can't go. There's a limit to how much you can simplify that system and still have it work. When you think about life, that's one of many interesting questions one would like to be able to really address in a broader, more general way.

Once we have such simulations, the ultimate hope is that they will give us a handle to develop theories, because over and over again in nature you see that unless you have some concrete, idealized system to which you apply your theories, you can't really make a good theory. You have to have something like that firmly in mind to which you attach your mathematical apparatus.

The experiments of Joule in thermodynamics really went a long way toward giving that to people like Clausias and Gibbs. Carnot is another example. Carnot and Joule provided the foundation that we needed to sort out the way heat moves around and even to define heat. It's hard to think that in the early part of the nineteenth century people didn't know what heat was, they only had vague ideas about it. That's the state we're in now when we talk about complex systems, life, structure, complexity, organization, and all these things. We bat them around as though we know what they are, but we really don't know what they are in the more precise sense that scientists like to have.

BROCKMAN: No doubt you've given some thought to the philosophical implications of your work. Could you talk about them?

LANGTON: The idea of artificially created life is pregnant for any branch of philosophy. I think it's true to say that, whether it happens in the next ten or a hundred or a thousand years, we're at the stage where it has become possible to create living things that are connected to us not so much by material as by information. In geological time, we're literally at the end of one era of evolution and at the beginning of another. It's easy to descend into fantasy at this point because we really don't know what's coming up. If, in the next two years, we create a robot that could survive on its own, that could go out and refine it's own materials to construct a copy of itself and could do so in such a way as to produce variants and evolve, we don't have any way of predicting the outcome. There are quite a few issues we need to think about and address before we do make such a device. A reporter once asked me how I would feel about my children living in an era where there was a lot of Artificial Life.

BROCKMAN: Maybe your children will be artificial?

LANGTON: Well, that was my answer. The children of the mind, to use Hans Moravac's phrase, or my biological children, are all going to be my children. We are going to be able to produce ideas that have a life of their own and I'm not going to even begin to try to parse that out in all the different philosophical questions. Clearly, there are a great deal of questions and issues that can be raised.

FARMER: People have always recognized just how fascinating it is that living organisms, human beings in particular, can do all the amazing things that they do, and they tend to assign mystical notions to this, such as soul and free will. These ideas mark how incredible it is that you can start with some thing that's built out of simple parts and somehow hook those parts together. Or those parts get hooked up by evolution through some spontaneous process, giving rise to all sorts of fascinating emergent behaviors that are difficult to reconcile with some nitty-gritty low-level description of what's happening.

To go back to this debate with Rupert Sheldrake, who characterizes himself as a vitalist, what I kept trying to tell him is that you can be a mechanist and a vitalist at the same time; they don't have to be mutually exclusive. A system that is completely mechanistic at some low level, because of nonlinear interactions between its parts, can give rise to fascinating emergent behavior that is very vital. I think it's a mistake to separate these points of view. As this whole area develops I hope a much clearer picture emerges, a more synthetic philosophy that allows somebody to be vitalist and mechanist at the same time, that doesn't denigrate the mystical properties of things but perhaps gives us a little more insight, another way of looking at what these things might be and prevents us from getting bogged down in silly and anthropomorphic questions. That's perhaps one of the most central ways in which these kinds of studies may help us sort out a more reasonable philosophy.

BROCKMAN: Isn't it a conceit of scientists to say that pure science is not anthropomorphic?

FARMER: Pure science is certainly anthropomorphic, but we're constantly peeling an onion and breaking into levels that are less mired down in that viewpoint than the previous level. When you jump from the Ptolomaic view to the Copernican view of the solar system, you've taken a small step toward making our human view of the universe less anthropomorphic because we've stepped out of the center in one aspect.

When we assign magical properties to ourselves, such as intelligence, that we refuse to assign to something else, then I think that as we are confronted with things that are overtly intelligent we will have to begin to accept that they are intelligent. Or, as we're confronted with things that are alive but out of the framework that gave rise to us, then I think it's one more layer of the onion of our anthropomorphic worldview getting peeled off, not to say that we've achieved some nonanthropomorphic view of the world, but that we've achieved some view of the world that is less anthropomorphic than the one that went before it.

I think human beings are learning as we go along not to place ourselves at the center or the pinnacle of everything that goes on in the world. With the advent of artificial life I think we will lose much of our monopoly on certain things ("we" meaning both people and the DNA-carbon–based organisms that we see all around us). On both these levels at once a certain sterile homogeneity will be lost.

LANGTON: It is going to be hard for people to accept that machines are as alive as they are, and that there's nothing special about human life that isn't achievable by any other kind of stuff out there, if you just put it together in the right way. It's going to be as hard for people to accept this idea as it was that we aren't at the center of the universe.

Another philosophical issue this raises is one of our own existence—our own reality and our own universe. After you work for a long time at creating these artificial universes and wondering about getting life going in them, you find yourself looking over your shoulder every now and then and wondering if there isn't yet another level on top of ours. This is Fredkin's view.

BROCKMAN: The human as artifice?

LANGTON: Or this universe as artifice in some other, much more real universe. Until now, biology has been based on taking apart what's already alive and, based on that, it tries to understand what life is. We're finding that you can learn a lot by trying to put things together, trying to create your own life, finding out what problems you run into. This notion of what you learn about your own universe by trying to build these simple models is nice, this notion of putting together an artificial universe. It makes me look over my shoulder and wonder, What sort of a universe am I really in?

A Journey
of Relativities

MARY CATHERINE BATESON
WITH
SEVANNE MARGARET KASSARJIAN

Each of us has the sense of both concurring with and differing from our respective generations, and we share a tradition of elaborating self-knowledge through observation and encounters with others, for all observation of the other is also self-observation. Less obviously, but still necessarily, all observation occurs in a Heraclitean flux in which the motion of the other is observed by the moving self; it is not only that the river flows but that the observer is in motion, stepping through the current.

In 1956 I went to Israel with my mother, Margaret Mead, who had been invited as a consultant on the assimilation of immigrants. Two days before we were supposed to leave Israel, I decided to stay and finish high school there in Hebrew. I remained for just over a year. That was the year of the Israeli campaign in Sinai and the Anglo-French invasion of Suez, the year of the Hungarian uprising. Eisenhower was President of the United States, Ben-Gurion was Prime Minister of Israel, and Khrushchev had just undertaken the de-Stalinization of the Soviet Union. I turned seventeen in the aftermath of the Sinai campaign.

In January 1988, thirty years later, I went back with my daughter, Vanni, eighteen years old and a freshman at Brown University. Together, we set out to explore the relationship between her vision and mine in the present, and between her vision now and mine at the same age, against the shifting backgrounds of time and place. Each of us has the sense of both concurring with and differing from our respective generations, and we share a tradition of elaborating self-knowledge through observation and encounters with others, for all observation of the other is also self-observation. Less obviously, but still necessarily, all observation occurs in a Heraclitean flux in which the motion of the other is observed by the moving self; it is not only that the river flows but that the observer is in motion, stepping through the current. Vanni and I had only three weeks, nearly the same time period my mother and I had in Israel before I decided to stay, but only a brief chance to test and feel the water's flow.

We are at a time of unfolding exploration of these relativities in anthropology as well as other disciplines. One dimension of this growing awareness has to do with the construction of an epistemology rooted in a renewed self-reference. For some, the exploration of self is a sufficient end. For others, the exploration of self is honed into a tool for understanding the other, through various forms of disciplined subjectivity and empathy. Perhaps because they have so often been told what they ought to think and feel, women have been pioneers in this new tuning of self-consciousness.

Underlying my curiosity about how my response and Vanni's would differ was the puzzlement I had felt in trying to unravel the curious muddle that surrounded Derek Freeman's 1983 attack[1] on my mother's book, *Coming of Age in Samoa*[2]: two different observers, one a man and one a woman, of different ages and backgrounds; two different Samoas, one American-governed and the other administered by New Zealand until 1962; fifty years' difference and therefore two different Americas. All anthropological work is rooted in comparison, all meaning in context, but Freeman's work was flawed by a stance of scientism that denied the necessary relativities. When *Coming of Age* came out in 1928, it was reviewed as highly titillating material, and Freeman apparently still finds it provocative; but if the journalists who made such a fuss had bothered to read the book itself, where it drifts now far down the Heraclitean stream, they would have found a different book, one about young people less pressured into early sexual activity than American teenagers today. The context for understanding sexuality has changed. Similarly, Israel gave me in 1956 to 1957 a paradigm for something I had found lacking in my own society: commitment. Between that experience and the American present lie the impassioned sixties and the seventies, the new noncommitment of the eighties, and my own efforts to find and sustain commitments. In Israel, there has been war after war, old ambiguities have deepened, a certain innocence has been lost.

I had told Vanni a miscellany of stories about the newly founded kibbutz I had visited in the Negev, where several of my classmates planned to spend their lives. When I was there, there were only a few tentative buildings, no trees, no children. Today there are many trees, and children of all ages, but the classmates whose dedication I treasured as a model over the years have almost all left. We also visited two older kibbutzim, hearing of pervasive worry about the kibbutz-born children who want to leave, about women who point out that in spite of the ideology of equality, jobs are gender-typed and leadership positions almost exclusively given to males, about the economic problems resulting from the withdrawal of subsidies, and the competition's relying on cheap labor from the refugee camps. I had told Vanni to take fresh clothes for Friday night, for surely there would be singing and dancing on the eve of the sabbath, but we were told that that hasn't happened for years. "Sometimes, though, the teenagers have a disco." Like me, the kibbutz movement has become middle-aged and ambivalent. I commented to a friend that members seemed not to greet one another on the paths, and he said that indeed they used to do so, but eventually they became fed up. I found the kibbutzniks reminiscent of faculty at a small New England liberal-arts college, an inward-looking community with a deep conviction of virtue, locked into perpetual intimacy by economic dependency, facing daily reminders of the petty conflicts and power plays of the decades. Something like a soured marriage, with many extra faces at the breakfast table. I left Israel in 1957 with my sense of its newness, of its youth that matched my own, untarnished, just as most college students graduate before the romance of college dims.

I went to a high school in the Jerusalem area, so my friends were not the sheltered children of the kibbutz but urban children committed to the agrarian socialist ideal. Vanni found it difficult to establish communication with the young people she met on the kibbutzim and responded with sharp skepticism and disappointment to a community that was indeed less committed and less sure of itself than it seemed to me thirty years ago. She was not doing research, of course, but recording impressions—the first impressions that give way before greater knowledge but are always valuable to record because they contain their own evanescent snatches of insight.

Ironically, in trying to express the sense of weakened commitment, Vanni drew on an image from the fifties, from the alienation of my own generation. In her notes on the trip, she wrote: "The next generation on the kibbutz is made up of kids who are not rebels without a cause. They are rebels without a clue. I know that's a harsh phrase, grabbing for a first, quick impression. On the kibbutz I saw kids whose options had been so suddenly widened that decisions became harder to make, not easier. The fights their parents fought to establish the kibbutz have been won, and it's been built and is working, but it has nowhere else to go and can't go on as it is. To survive in the present, it finds itself undermining the ideology upon which it was based. But the contemporary options are yet to be grasped, much less accepted.

"The next generation doesn't know much about the world around them—it seems to come as a surprise," her notes continue. "The kids are forced to serve for two or three years in the army of a country that is constantly at war and can find itself no peace or uncontested ground on which to stand. They feel guilty if they don't want to serve in the army, and yet, if they do serve, they feel unsure of what they are fighting and serving for. Some have convinced themselves that they are wasting the two best and most important years of their lives for studying or seeing the world, or whatever. And yet the members of this next generation are expected to stay on the kibbutz, not to try something new, with some new knowledge they might obtain in travel or through study, but to maintain the old vision. If they don't, they are the ones corrupting and forgetting the ideology. To get the kids to stay, the kibbutz is offering them more and more bits of conveniences as inducements—they are even offering to pay for more extended trips away from the kibbutz to get people to stay. That is so fundamentally backward, it must point to a basic warping that has happened over time.

"The kibbutz seems to me to be representative of so many other things that start out idealistically—rather simple ideals, really—and inevitably fall through. But perhaps I should be congratulating them for still existing, that they have increased and multiplied, that they are supporting their members one way or another, and some are still fighting vehemently for shreds of the original ideology. The situation's not really all that bad at this very moment; it's the future that looks dim."

Perhaps the teenagers I knew were more like the group Vanni met in Tel Aviv. Less involved in ideology than the Israeli teenagers I knew thirty years ago, burdened by the ambiguities created by Israel's repression of protest in the occupied territories, which we heard about in each day's news, they still seemed to Vanni to have a core of commitment, mixed in with cynicism. She saw the cynicism as a strengthening element of realism. I'm not sure that in my time I would have seen it that way.

"It seemed somehow that Israel as a whole had an incredible dose of commitment. I felt as if the commitment came out of an awareness that seemed *forced on* the kibbutz kids and *adopted by* the Tel Aviv kids. The kibbutz kids seem to be fighting too hard to reconcile themselves to their future. Everything in their life has been idealistic; now, they are suddenly being given choices. They are smart and committed but they are forcing themselves into that future with this characteristic vigor and commitment, without the equipment they need to deal with it. One tool they especially seem to lack is a kind of patience that comes out of cynicism—or reality, I guess—which could keep them committed to a degree of growth and progress but hold them back from killing themselves if things don't all fall into place before they are twenty-five—if they don't make it big, shall we say, or find an ideal community. All these things like success are terribly relative, but somehow the Tel Aviv kids have a kind of perspective lacking in the kibbutz kids. The Tel Aviv kids I met are aware and intelligent and committed, too, but somehow it is all coming from different sources in a different order. They are growing up in a characteristically very committed and aware society, but without the huge doses of idealism. They are intelligent and concerned about their education and their future, but an element of their awareness reconciles them to the fact of problems like the years in the army. They seem to be taking things much more in stride, while on the kibbutz every option or change involves a decision that seems to shake their foundations."

One of the things Vanni reacted to most strongly and negatively was the utopian aspect of the kibbutz, the expectation that it might really be expected to achieve such goals as equality between the sexes. "Who doesn't have that problem? Why are they acting as if it could be solved for them right away? What makes them so special, and what about the thousands who have been trying for years? The kibbutz women should be thankful that they have work and people around they can talk to and all sorts of common services. Their future is at least mappable, so they know they will be fed and clothed and will have a place for their children and a place to grow old." Some of the very hopes that made possible the building of the kibbutzim and of Israel itself have turned into ironies, for the Israelis have been blind-sided by their own human frailty. Much as they complain that Israel is sometimes expected to meet higher standards than other nations, which it is, the occurrence of brutality in the army or corruption in the judiciary is greeted with surprised innocence. Perhaps if Judaism included a traditional belief like original sin, the founders would have taken advantage of the era of consensus to write a constitution. A friend commented to us when we visited Yad Vashem that now when she goes there with a visitor she finds herself reflecting on the potential for evil in every society.

Vanni's disappointment on the kibbutz was partly the result of multiple prisms of observation. Hearing my reminiscences as they were filtered over the years, she interpreted them against her own best models of excitement and commitment, summers of ardent effort in theater. "I couldn't help but look forward to my mother's memories. A kibbutz was going to be a small community of teeming energy, like camp or summer-stock theater. Everyone would be doing what they wanted to be doing, and because of that they would be doing it well. Everyone would be inspired by a common cause, and because of that it would be a united and self-perpetuating community of many facets and blossoming strengths. I guess in a way the romantic view of the kibbutz I had adopted from my mother's memories grew in my mind to represent Israel as a whole. Idealistically—that's how I thought everybody lived.

"But I don't think the memories that my mother helped to instill in me were the ones she left with thirty years ago. Thirty years is a long time, and I'm sure her mind and heart and romantic and dramatic senses used that time to get the most out of those memories. I also don't think when she was here things were as wonderful and idyllic as the images my mind has conjured up, because things just aren't. Probably I would be more positive about the kibbutz if I hadn't thought about it beforehand. And I think her original decision to stay had more to do with not wanting to go back home to her high school than with what was in Israel. She just happened to get lucky and really blossom in the situation she found herself in. That's a difference between us—she was coming to the end of high school and wanting to do something new. I'm already into my first year at college, at the beginning of the next phase. I don't think my mom has decided yet whether she is glad that she has had no contact in thirty years or not.

"I can't even imagine thirty years.

"I'm constantly struggling with the idea of commitment. For some reason I've happened to choose an interest or a profession or a future, whatever it turns out to be, which complicates things even more. Theater is what I care about. I can be sure that I have a degree of skill and commitment. Whether it is intrinsic in my character or something I have learned, I don't know, or how long my potential for learning will keep going. I also have no idea whether I have the kibbutz perspective or the Tel Aviv perspective. But somehow I do have something, some kind of commitment, even though it's mixed with questions and self-doubt. A lot of the people around me at college seem really lackadaisical. I have friends who have no idea where they are going or how they are going to get there, and I have grown-ups telling me that I still have to discover 'my life and my future.' Then they look at me with a glance that says, 'Poor child, she really thinks she's interested in the theater.' But I've always thought that theater was a much better thing for me to be interested in than people gave me credit for. Besides all of my own ideals about theater as a medium for communicating the human experience, a truthful art and craft, I also like to think that there are so many different tributaries to the theater—anthropology, psychology, et cetera—that somewhere there will be room for me; it's a profession of misfits anyway. So I do have that comfort. I have the impression that my mother didn't have a comfort like that when she was my age."

Hmm. As Vanni juxtaposes her perceptions with what she has heard from me, I have to struggle to recover and evaluate memories. I know that the question of commitment was central to my falling in love with Israel. I was cynical about any commitment to my own culture, or to any elements of nation or religion I had been exposed to. I remember quarreling with my mother in a hotel room in Athens, before we flew to Israel, about whether there was anything in America to believe in. She thought there was, was always patriotic. I know I felt like a misfit, writing poetry and coming from an odd part of town and an odd kind of family. And I know that when I left Israel to go to college I took an aching sense of loss and envy of my friends who followed their certainties into the army. But even when I daydreamed about the possibility of living on a kibbutz, I felt I would not want to raise children there. I'd be glad enough of a communal nursery and a communal kitchen, but I believe that ideal communities—or any imagined "way of perfection"—must be chosen anew by each generation, not biologically recruited. Indeed, I believe increasingly that lifetime commitments modeled on marriage, the commitment to a kibbutz as well as the commitment to a monastery, should have the same open doors that marriage has come to have—right for one phase of life, for ten years or twenty, but not necessarily binding for sixty. We are only just discovering the harvest of creativity from the departures and new commitments of the extended life cycle.

"For most of my friends at college, commitment has to do with the future. If they are like me they are committed to something because of what they see at the end of the tunnel—med school, politics, disarmament, marriage, theater . . . but some American kids are simply committed to the future with nothing to get them there. They just have this intense belief that eventually it will come and they will have their life. It will all work itself out eventually: their hopes, their parents' expectations, the bills they will have to pay. Israeli kids are committed to the present. If they are on a kibbutz they are obsessed with reconciling their position there *now.* If they are in the army they are constantly aware of their contribution to their country *now*; if they are traveling they want to see the whole world *now.*"

I asked Vanni what she was hearing from her age mates about the trouble in the occupied territories, and whether they understood that the new round of protests and repressions represented an irreversible change. "Well, they are practical and confident but really unsure of final stands. They tend to spend a lot of time reasoning things out: 'How can we hate the Arabs . . . ? They are in a similar position to us . . . but how can they blow up innocent people . . . ? Of course they are innocent, but if I was a soldier and an Arab started throwing stones I'd want to shoot back. . . .' I asked one kid, 'Why doesn't everyone realize that nothing will be accomplished unless you at least talk it out and compromise?' And he said, 'It's easy for you to sit here, you're not on the front line.' ('You never have been and you never will be' was also in his voice.) You can hear the practicality and the commitment, but there is also this sense of helplessness, always, in people's voices. Their voices build up and then they finish their sentences on a high note, sort of questioning. But also in the voice is this confidence that life will go on—normal life seems to be what the kids want most. I'm not sure they really imagine things coming to a head."

When fighting started in 1956, many of my friends hoped this might be the last time war would be necessary, but today conflict has become habitual as the grandchildren of Palestinian refugees face the grandchildren of pioneers.

Another way in which Vanni's view and my own first response necessarily differed was in previous knowledge of the Middle East. Israel was the first Middle Eastern country in my experience, but already when I left I was determined to learn Arabic and to understand the Arab side of the story, and much of my life since then has been involved with the Middle East. Vanni has grown up within this unfolding involvement. Her father is Armenian and she spent much of her childhood in Iran, visiting relatives in Beirut as long as it was possible to do so. In the flea market in Jaffa we found we could get better prices than our Israeli friends—because almost all the merchants are Iranian Jews. In the Old City of Jerusalem we asked our way in Arabic to the lovely serene mosques on the Temple Mount, where troops used tear gas two days later. And in the Armenian Quarter we found an official of the patriarchate who opened for us the Church of Saint James and showed us personally around the diminutive Armenian Museum, with its documentation of the Armenian diaspora and massacres, in curious counterpoint to the overwhelming and superbly mounted exhibits at Yad Vashem and the Museum of the (Jewish) Diaspora in Tel Aviv. When I went to Israel I had a sense of lacking cultural roots, but Vanni could trace roots of her own there: One of the patriarchate buildings was used as an orphanage after the Armenian massacres, and there Vanni's great-uncle was brought after being rescued from the desert, and there he was trained to play in the orphanage band and carried off by Crown Prince Haile Selassie to be raised in the Ethiopian court.

In 1957 I visited the refugee camps in Jordan, and since then I have been unable to see the questions of Israel and Palestine with an undivided mind. Vanni will never see them that way and never make the mistake of singling out the Holocaust from all the sorry history of human inhumanity.

Israel has always had a complex layering of intergenerational conflict. Already when I was there, the Israeli-born sabras were visibly impatient with the diaspora tradition and with reminders of the Holocaust, preoccupied with building something new. Today many young people who would like to emulate their parents in pioneering departures find that this means criticizing or even leaving the kibbutz or Israel rather than settling into the compromises of continuity. It is not easy for children whose parents invented their own models simply to follow in parental footsteps. No easier for Vanni launching out into the world of theater than for the children of the kibbutz.

Vanni wound up her first batch of notes, halfway through the visit, by writing: "I didn't mean to undermine so harshly my mother or the kibbutz or Israel, but I did. I guess it's just a backlash from my hopes." By the time we left she was more positive, but it seemed clear that Israel would not be for her, as it has been for me and so many others, a parable of possibility. Instead, it has become a symbol of the need to keep struggling in spite of ambiguity. Vanni seems to me far more than one year wiser than my remembered self of thirty years ago, and yet I have been accompanied in all life's compromises since that time by Israel's image of hope.

NOTES

[1] Derek Freeman, *Margaret Mead and Samoa: The Making and Unmaking of an Anthropological Myth* (Cambridge: Harvard University Press, 1983).

[2] Margaret Mead, *Coming of Age in Samoa: A Psychological Study of Primitive Youth for Western Civilization* (New York: William Morrow, 1928).

Johnny Can't Read
(And Neither Can His Old Man)

ROGER SCHANK

The goal is not to teach reading at all. It is to teach children to be able to gather information and be critical in their understanding of that information. Naturally, books are excellent sources of new information. But in the computer age they are by no means the only source. The goal is thinking, questioning, analysis, and synthesis, not reading.

Should children learn how to read? No, just kidding. Even in the age of the computer, reading is still a valuable skill. Surely reading will be with us forever. Well, that may not be so certain, not because the medium will become unworkable, but because there may not be so many interesting books to read. Best seller lists full of self-help books, how-to books, sex and diet books, and books of advice from famous comedians make it clear that real reading has been passé for some time. Books that challenge their readers to think about something don't sell a million copies, or even a few thousand. Why this state of affairs? The answer may be complex, striking at the roots of our society in a technological age, but one thing seems possible: People may not know how to read.

Why can't Johnny read? For one thing, no one ever really taught him to. For another, what he was taught as reading so distorted his view of the subject and the possible pleasure he might derive from it that he gave it up as soon as possible.

Part of the problem comes from the fact that understanding is not taught, while reading is. What's the difference? It is difficult to imagine what it would mean to teach reading without teaching understanding. It doesn't even seem possible. And, in fact, it isn't. But this hasn't stopped the schools from trying. Reading instruction in school tends to revolve around the *mechanics* of reading—syllables, prefixes, and so on—while understanding could be taught as well by discussing movies or having conversations. In a movie of moderate depth, following what is going on entails figuring out who is doing what and why. Such details are not always spelled out in a movie since doing so would make the movie tedious. Viewers are assumed to be intelligent enough to fill in the details about motivations themselves; they are also expected to make some assumptions about what is going to happen next. A good movie often violates those assumptions.

Part of understanding a movie, then, involves a process of thinking. The more complex the movie, the more thinking is involved. The same is true of reading. Books in which everything is spelled out and all future actions in the book are obvious from the start don't make great literature. Reading, or at least intelligent reading, the kind that involves thinking on behalf of the reader, requires understanding of the most complex sort.

It seems obvious that if the basis of reading is understanding, and understanding and learning to understand is the fun part of what the process of learning to read is about, then teaching reading should mean teaching understanding. And one could teach reading, to children who don't already know the mechanics of reading, by introducing movies into reading classes.

What does it mean for someone to understand? Is it really necessary to teach this? Why isn't decoding the letter combinations into words what reading is all about? To see that it isn't, read the following story:

John went to Lutèce last night. He had the lobster.

Now I am going to give you a reading-comprehension test. Your question is: *What did John eat last night?*

Can you answer it? How do you know that what you answered was correct? The story never says a word about eating. It doesn't mention restaurants, it doesn't mention that John was hungry. Somehow, we just know that the answer to the question I asked is obvious. And we know that, had the story said *He had the car* instead of *He had the lobster*, we would not even for a minute think that he ate his car. How do we do all this?

When we teach Johnny to read, we do not, nor need we, teach him that people eat lobsters but not cars. Nevertheless, this information, and a lot more like it, is an important part of what reading or understanding is about.

We can specify two distinct aspects of the reading process that have consequences for the teaching of reading. The first is the association of a sound with a given set of letters. The teaching of word recognition takes place in the early grades. By the second grade, most children can read simple words in isolation. From that point on, many school systems invest most of their effort in the second aspect of the reading process. It is hard to put a name to this second part; many schools call it "language" or "language arts." Lumped together under this rubric are such diverse items as spelling, syllabification, and alphabetization. It is at this point that children, no matter how well (or how poorly) they have done in learning to decode the symbols that represent words on the printed page, begin to get bored with reading. Instead of teaching children to understand better, we teach them to play with language.

What does one do during the reading process? Since reading is, after all, primarily comprehension, the key question to ask is: What is a person doing when attempting to "understand"? A large part of the understanding process is the attempt to make explicit what is implicit in a sentence, or in a situation in general. Language is a means of conveying information. But frequently what is expressed in an actual sentence is only a small part of what the speaker wishes to convey. Often, much of the intended information is implicit. It is the job of our memories to fill in what has been left out.

When we hear someone say that he or she likes a book, it is our memory processes that are responsible for determining that this probably means he or she liked reading the book, as opposed to holding it, for example. When we hear that John likes Mary, we can speculate that he might ask Mary for a date, if other aspects of the situation fit the rest of a pattern that we know about such things. Such additional information comes from our memories and is incorporated into our understanding of what we hear. We learn to make guesses or predictions about what we hear. We learn to make details of what we have been told. In reading, these same *guesses* apply.

This predicted information also tells us what *not* to think, in regard to what we have been told. Notice that the expectation that John will want to read Mary does not come to mind. But what is the actual surface difference between *John likes books* and *John likes Mary*? The difference between them relates to what we know about the world. It is not explained solely by saying that there are two different senses of *like*.

But talking about the different senses of *like* is what teachers like to teach in school. The concepts of synonym, antonym, and such can be taught, and students can be easily tested to see if they learned the material. But what is the relevant material? In this case, it is whatever enhances reading. Here, the fact is, a child already knows about the two senses of *like*, and needn't be taught any of it. Instead of teaching children to read, we are teaching them to take tests that force them to make explicit what they already know implicitly about their language.

Each word's meaning affects the meaning of the words surrounding it. To decide on the correct choice of a meaning for a word, it is necessary to understand it in terms of the partially composed meaning of the entire sentence. For example, the meaning of *straw* is different in each of the next two sentences, as is the meaning of *plane* in the following two:

Sip your soda with a straw.

Lie down on that straw.

I took the plane to New York.

I used the plane in the garage.

Words have multiple possible meanings. Because of this we can never simply say: "The meaning of this word is such and such." The context that surrounds a word determines its meaning. This is true to such an extent that even in the preceding examples, we can reverse the meanings of the word *plane* simply by supplying a new sentence that provides a different context:

John needs to do some woodworking.
I took the plane to New York.

How did you get to New York?
I used the plane in the garage.

Do we need to teach people how to do this? How did you do it? People don't even see the ambiguities inherent in what they read. Of course, to be an educated person it is nice to know something about how the language one uses every day actually works. But, in order to read, one need know none of it.

To figure out correctly what these sentences mean, one has to have had the experience associated with them. So what if Johnny can make the right sounds when he sees *plane*? The question is: Does he have enough experience to guide him through these situations? If he had had no experience with either *plane*, no sounding out of the words is going to help, except to make him *sound* as if he knows what's going on.

In a sense, then, the reading process relies more heavily on one's memory of what has gone on in the past than it does on the words on the printed page. Consider the sentence: *John needs some aspirin for his cold.* We can read the words easily enough, but not to be found anywhere on the page is the fact that John intends to swallow this aspirin and that he believes aspirin cures colds. To know both of those things one has to know that the action and the belief implicit in that sentence are normal enough and follow from the concept of need in the context of medicine.

Contrast this sentence with *John needs some money for his son.* It is the same sentence, at least grammatically, but John isn't going to swallow anything, and we know nothing about his beliefs about sickness, although we may be able to guess something of his philosophy of child-raising. And what do we teach in school about such things? We teach how to parse the sentence to discover that these sentences have the same structure. A lot of use that will be later on in life. We don't attempt to teach the process of how to draw conclusions about what people believe from observing their actions. That process is what is necessary here in order to understand what the sentence means.

What matters in understanding is *inference making*. Inference making is the process of making best guesses about what a speaker must have meant apart from what he said explicitly. So, although the sentence does not say that John intends to put the aspirin in his mouth and swallow it, that is a very good guess (though it may turn out to be wrong). When actions aren't stated, we need to figure them out for ourselves.

When the goals of a character aren't stated, we need to figure them out as well. When we are told that someone wants to do something, we must ask ourselves why if we want to understand what is going on. To convince yourself of this, consider a story like: *John loved Mary. Somebody mugged Mary in the park. When John heard about this he was satisfied.* It is difficult here to explain John's reaction. The only way we can do so is by imagining some of John's and Mary's goals and seeking some explanation of how mugging may have been in concert with some goal of John's. The story is peculiar because the proposition that the mugging could have a good effect is peculiar. Of course, there would have been no problem had *was satisfied* been replaced by *cried*. But in the latter case we would have no conscious remembrance of searching our memories for the coherence of the goals and actions of the characters in the story, because crying is not an unusual response to the situation. But, conscious or not, an important part of the understanding process is the identification of goals, and the recognition that goals are connected to the actions intended to achieve them.

So, what does all this tell us about how to teach children to read? First, we must get rid of the idea that children enter the first grade as empty-headed beings. Of course, no teacher would actually say that he or she believed that, but this does not stop the school system from teaching children to make explicit what they already know quite well. By the age of six, most children speak their language very well. And, although they may be illiterate, they are not ignorant. They possess large vocabularies, know a great deal about the syntactic structures of their language, and have a tremendous amount of information about the world.

One of the very important tasks of reading instructors is to assess what children know so that they can build upon it. Note that here I am referring to a child's knowledge of the outside world rather than knowledge of either reading or language. Actually, the problem I am referring to can be understood by considering many other tasks that require understanding but have nothing to do with reading. For example, six-year-olds will only understand the barest parts of a movie that is not intended specifically for them because they do not have the requisite knowledge of the world.

Compounding this problem of knowledge assessment for the

teacher of reading is the problem of assessing what children know of their language. Children who speak well, for example, will have implicitly learned a great deal about the rules of their language. For example, it may seem quite reasonable to teachers of reading to teach children about words ending in "ly" or "er," but most children in the early grades already use such endings in their speech. Furthermore, they understand words that have such endings. They do not have *explicit* knowledge of the meanings of those endings, they don't know the word *suffix*, and probably never should, but that does not mean they lack that knowledge *implicitly*. That is, the kind of knowledge children need to help them read words with those endings is already present. There is no reason to teach children to have explicit knowledge of what they know implicitly.

What does an adult know that a child of six does not? On the face of it, this seems like a silly question. An adult has a sophisticated knowledge of the whole world; a child understands only a small part of what is present in the immediate environment. What does an adult know, then, that enables him or her to read what a six-year-old does not know? Or, to put this a bit differently, what is it that an adult who reads literature knows that one who can only read how-to books doesn't?

Reading means understanding, and understanding involves at least the following processes:

1. Making simple inferences
2. Establishing causal connections
3. Recognizing stereotyped situations
4. Predicting and generating plans
5. Tracking people's goals
6. Recognizing thematic relationships between individuals and society
7. Employing beliefs about the world in understanding
8. Accessing and utilizing raw facts

These eight kinds of knowledge roughly categorize what an adult knows about the world. A child in the first grade has this knowledge,

too, but in a simplified form. Teaching understanding means enhanc-
ing this ability to rely upon knowledge of the world to help interpret
what is going on.

The eight types of knowledge just listed help a reader to interpret
what he or she hears, sees, and reads, which in turn helps him or her
determine the import of what has been read. Let's consider the
knowledge involved, according to these eight categories, in reading a
simple story:

> John hated his boss. He went to the bank and got twenty dollars. He
> bought a gun. The next day at work he decided to ask his boss for a
> raise. But John was so upset by his own plan that he told his boss he
> was sick and went home and cried.

This is a simple story, on the surface. The words are easy and most
third-graders would have very little difficulty reading the story out
loud. Yet very few of them would feel they had understood it. Beneath
the surface of some simple words are some complicated ideas that
require an adult's understanding of the world to interpret. Let me
illustrate just some of the ways in which each of these eight categories
comes into play:

1. Inferences. In order to understand a sentence fully, it is necessary to
draw conclusions from that sentence about the things that were not
explicitly stated but that nevertheless are true. We must *read between
the lines.* People are rarely aware that they are making an inference at
any given time. They are much more aware that they have made one
when that inference is violated or in error for some reason.

Some inferences necessary for understanding the above story are:

a. After buying the gun, John has the gun—that is, buying implies
    having.
b. The gun cost twenty dollars—that is, buying requires money.
c. John intends to use the gun—that is, one buys something for its
    eventual use.
d. John will threaten or possibly shoot someone—that is, functional
    objects (such as guns) are used for specific purposes.

2. *Causal Connections.* Adults have an understanding of how one event relates to another. There are many different kinds of causal relations. Adults attempt to determine the causal relationships inherent in what they are trying to understand. (This category and the others described below can all be seen as different varieties of inference.)

One causal relationship in the above story is:

Going to the bank enabled John to get money—that is, "going" can suggest actions that ordinarily take place at the destination.

3. *Stereotyped Situation.* People have a great deal of information about stereotyped situations. In this story those that are referred to are banks, stores (the place where John bought the gun), and offices. Understanding this story requires a working knowledge of how the real world functions.

4. *Plan Prediction and Generation.* To understand this story fully, it is necessary to postulate a set of possible plans under which John is likely to be operating. In order to postulate such plans, however, one has to be able to generate them oneself. The more that John's actions seem to the reader to fit into a coherent plan of action, the more "understandable" the story seems. This plan-creation and understanding ability are at the heart of following a story of this kind. This is precisely where a third-grader will be severely handicapped when trying to understand the story. Even the simplest of plans is hard to follow if one has not learned how to follow another person's plan.

5. *Goal Tracking.* What is John going to do, and why is he doing it? These are the questions that occur as we read this story. However, answering such questions requires knowing about goals such as being well treated, respected, well paid, or whatever complex set of goals are reasonable to postulate in understanding this story.

6. *Thematic Relationships.* Understanding this story requires a good assessment of how an employee might feel toward a boss, and an interpretation of hatred in this context. A third-grader may know what "hate" means to him or her, but such a definition is likely to be

only partially relevant. Another important thematic relationship is the fear of being an outcast, an immoral person, or a criminal, all of which one can imagine to be going through John's mind.

7. *Beliefs.* We, as readers, believe certain things about what is right and wrong. If John is going to threaten his boss for a raise, or possibly kill him, we view it at least as misguided, and probably terribly wrong. These beliefs about what is a correct course of action in the world are very much a part of how we understand, and thus of how we read.

8. *Raw Facts.* Banks have money. Bosses give raises. Crying releases tension. Stores sell guns. All these are simple facts about the world, without which it would be hard to understand this story.

We are now ready to return to our three-year-old. What does he or she know of the world? What, within the range of these eight kinds of knowledge, is available to children to help them understand?

1. Inferences. By age three a child can make some very simple inferences. He knows that if you put something someplace, it will be there; that if you eat, you won't be hungry anymore, and so on. Recall that the ability to make inferences is dependent upon world knowledge in the first place. So, while the basic apparatus is there by age three, the only things that a child of this age can infer are those things about which he already has a good understanding, things within the child's small world.

Teaching a child to read, therefore, means teaching him to figure out what else is true besides what he was told. But whatever one teaches in this regard is likely to be fallacious, at least some of the time. Teaching what is true of the world is a subjective matter at best. Inference of the sort we are talking about is not logical in any sense. These same inference problems exist in watching movies; a story is a story, and understanding a complicated one requires that we infer.

2. Causal Connections. A three-year-old child has a very confused view of what causes what. At age three a child is willing to believe just about anything with respect to causality. Because of this, the child often cannot make the correct causal connections in what she reads.

Can you teach causality? I think so. Further, teaching how to assess a chain of reasoning or a physical chain of events is a very important part of teaching thinking. It is also a part of reading. Authors leave the chains of reasoning to the reader to fill in. The sequence *John hit Mary; she died* means that she died because of the hit. On the other hand, *John hit Mary; she laughed* doesn't mean that the hit caused the laugh in the same sense that hitting can cause death. Do children know this? Not so well. And they cannot read without knowing it.

3. *Stereotyped Situations.* Children do, on the other hand, have very sophisticated ideas about stereotypical action sequences, or *scripts.* There is evidence to suggest that children are forming scripts almost from birth. An example of a script is the restaurant script or the airplane-ride script. These scripts tell us who does what when and what we must do to play our part. Children learn all kinds of scripts, from ones about diaper-changing to their own version of the restaurant script, which misses a great deal of what is really going on in a restaurant but does get them fed. The scripts that they form are discarded or improved as the case warrants, a process that serves as one basis for learning. Thus, by age four a child has very good and detailed knowledge, albeit from his own point of view and experiences, of such stereotyped situations as banks, grocery stores, mealtimes, and restaurants.

Consider a conversation between a Parent (P) and a four-year-old (C):

P: Now, I want you to tell me what happens when you go to a restaurant.

C: Okay.

P: What happens in a restaurant? Start at the beginning.

C: You come in and you sit down at the table. And then the waitress comes. And she gives you a menu. And then she takes it back and writes down your order. And then you eat what she gave you. And then you get up from the table. And you pay the money and then you walk out of the store.

4. *Plans.* A child of three does very little planning that is not extremely simple. Consequently, she cannot track someone else's plans very well. By the age of six, a child's ability to plan for herself is greatly improved, but understanding someone else's plan can still be quite difficult. Consider the following story that was read to the same four-year-old. She was asked questions about the story. Notice her answers indicate a strong reliance on script-based knowledge and a failure to comprehend fully the plans of the characters in the story:

> John loved Mary, but she didn't want to marry him. One day, a dragon stole Mary from the castle. John got on top of his horse and killed the dragon. Mary agreed to marry him. They lived happily ever after.

P: Why did John kill the dragon?
C: 'Cause it was mean.
P: What was mean about it?
C: It was hurting him.
P: How did it hurt him?
C: It was probably throwing fire at him.
P: Why did Mary agree to marry John?
C: 'Cause she loved him very much and he wanted very much to marry her.
P: What was going to happen to Mary?
C: If what?
P: When the dragon got her?
C: She would get dead.
P: Why would the dragon do that?
C: 'Cause it wanted to eat her.
P: How come Mary decided to marry John, when she wouldn't in the beginning?
C: That's a hard question.
P: Well, what do you think the answer is?
C: 'Cause then she just didn't want him and then he argued very much and talked to her a lot about marrying her and then she got interested in marrying her . . . I mean him.

The problem of planning is, for children, the single biggest obstacle in reading. It is also a big obstacle in watching a movie and in observing what their parents are doing. Adults follow complex plans and they also learn cues by which to identify one another's plans. Without information about the kinds of plans there are, how can a child understand that when a character in a movie goes to the perfume store and he is in love, it means one thing, but if he is very angry and goes to the liquor store, it means another?

5. *Goals.* As with plans, a child's goals are so simple that he has almost no ability to understand that someone else might have more complex goals, much less be able to track someone else's goals. This is a very important point in considering what stories are appropriate for children at any given age. If a child cannot understand the goals of the characters, in the deepest sense of understanding, he will not be able to follow the story being read, no matter how simple the vocabulary and syntax of that story.

6. *Thematic Relationships.* A child understands certain thematic relationships in which she herself is involved. She knows about what mothers and fathers do, for example. But her knowledge of the role of the grocer or the bus driver is much more limited. She has only the vaguest notions about the aspects of their roles that do not relate directly to her. A child may not realize that a doctor gets money for what she does, for example. Other thematic relationships, such as those involving dishonesty or malevolence, will be totally unclear to a three-year-old. Stories that use such relationships will be difficult for a young child to comprehend fully.

7. *Beliefs.* A child's beliefs are constantly changing. Here again, story understanding must relate to beliefs the child actually holds, if he is to understand a story. Or, he must be taught about the beliefs of others. Understanding how different cultures view the world must be an important part of education. Sometimes such things are taught in school, but usually in a social-studies class. Reading depends upon being able to figure out the beliefs of others. Consider the following story:

The preparations were made for the tribal puberty rite. Little Nkomo
was frightened and he grabbed his mother's hand. The crowd drew
back in horror.

A reader doesn't know what rule Nkomo violated, but he can guess.
Such guessing is an important part of reading.

8. *Raw Facts.* The child has quite a few of these. One reason to read is
to gather new facts. Without a healthy assortment of facts at one's
disposal, it is difficult to understand what is going on.

Of course, in learning to read, the child must first learn to recognize words on the printed page. After that, the fundamentals of
comprehending what people are doing and why they are doing it are
of more use in learning to read than any of the more traditional things
taught in reading instruction. Why aren't such things taught? Why
isn't there a course in understanding people? Here again, this is a
suggestion that flies in the face of how the school system operates.
Schools need facts to teach so that exams can be given. Children need
to learn to figure out what is going on in situations they haven't
encountered previously. They need to learn to reason in order to read
(and in order to do quite a bit else as well).

And what is actually taught when children learn *language arts*?
Here is a partial list of the units covered in the third and fourth grades
in language arts:

1. The use of dictionaries
2. Punctuation
3. Prefixes and suffixes
4. Compound words
5. Reading with expression
6. Using an index
7. Reading a diagram
8. Synonyms and antonyms
9. Making an outline
10. Spelling

11. Syllabification
12. Capitalization
13. Rules of grammar

Although I make no argument that some of these things should not be taught in the schools, there is a vast difference between teaching them and teaching reading. Units on each of these subjects are interrupted by endless reading comprehension tests. So, if learning to read isn't one long SAT test for a child, it is an examination on exciting things like the catalog system in the library.

There are two questions worth addressing here:

1. Do these thirteen items have anything to do with reading?

2. Is learning to read adversely affected by coupling "language arts" with reading?

None of the thirteen items has anything directly to do with reading. Some of them are clearly new skills (using an index, using a dictionary, making an outline). But these new skills should be dissociated from the teaching of reading. Many people read very well but have little or no familiarity with indexes or outlines. Coupling these skills with the teaching of reading can make reading itself seem dull or, even worse, difficult. Advancing in reading is often tied to advancing through workbooks that drill children in these skills, and the child who reads well can get bored and irritated with "learning to read."

In order to see why the teaching of reading and "language arts" must be separated, we must consider the distinction between recognition memory and recall memory. This distinction is crucial for understanding what we are doing when we teach reading.

People exhibit two distinct memory capabilities. They can recognize an object, and they can recall information when they need it. Some examples of the differences between recognition and recall are:

1. We can recognize somebody we know when we see that individual, but often it is difficult to conjure up the person's image (recall the image) when the person is not present.

2. We can recognize the capital of Norway, say, when we see it in a list of three on a multiple-choice test, but we cannot recall it without those choices before us.

3. We can find our way to a place we have been only once or twice, by recognizing various clues on the way (following our noses). After we turn right at a certain corner, we are sure that that was the right thing to do, but we could never have recalled the name of that street or the identifying landmarks well enough to tell someone else how to get there.

4. We can recognize somebody we know, yet forget his or her name or occupation.

These experiences are common to everyone, because of the "division" in our memories. This division is not a literal one. There are not two different memory boxes that contain the information we need. Rather, we are relying upon two different processes for retrieving information from memory.

To see this, imagine that you are the director of a large museum with five thousand rooms, each containing one hundred art objects. As director, you might have some difficulty specifying exactly where in the museum the "blue-and-white Ming vase with butterflies on it" is located. You might have a good idea about where it would most likely be found, and where to start looking. But 500,000 items are just too many for any person to know offhand the exact location of each. On the other hand, if you were put in the correct room, you would have no trouble identifying it as such without actually having to see the vase.

Searching the human memory in a thorough manner is actually much more difficult than searching a museum. At least in a museum there is a known organization of material. Some people are better organized than others, and they would be better at recall than others. Recognition, on the other hand, is more directly correlated with knowledge. The more one knows, the more one can recognize.

Now let us return to the teaching of reading. How are these two types of memory-retrieval processes related to reading? Spelling is an example of recall memory. When my daughter was five, she hung a sign on her door that read: NOBODE ALOUD. She could read extremely well at five. However, as noted, recognition and recall are very different processes. Reading is a recognition process; spelling, a recall process. To read we must recognize each word. To do this we must rely on our prior knowledge to help us. Having seen a word before, it is easier to recognize it. We do not need to use recall in the process of word recognition. To spell, we must find the correct spelling in memory. Thus, my daughter could write NOBODE by sounding out in her mind *nobody* and writing letters for sounds. Naturally she wrote E for the sound that that letter makes. But if she had been asked to read what she wrote, she might have said "no bode," since she well knew the rules for word recognition in the sounding out of new words.

Despite the fact that spelling and reading rely on totally different memory processes, they are often coupled in reading workbooks and school curricula. But the ability to read really does not depend upon the ability to spell. (There are many eminent professors who can hardly spell, but no one doubts their ability to read! In some school systems, such professors would have a difficult time being promoted from the third grade.)

Capitalization and punctuation are two skills, certainly quite valuable ones, that relate to the distinction between recognition and recall. Capitalization and punctuation are taught to children as recall phenomena, even though they by now know how to treat them as recognition phenomena. A child can read a punctuated text—that is, recognize it—without necessarily being able to punctuate a text. Learning to punctuate correctly is very difficult, even for adults. It should be taught as a subject in school, but, as the inability to punctuate properly does not affect one's reading ability, it should be taught separately from reading. Learning to punctuate is a recall phenomenon. In fact, all writing is a recall phenomenon, so this same argument applies to capitalization. Here again, recall phenomena must be differentiated from reading. Reading is a recognition process.

To deal with the remaining subjects on the preceding list, it will be necessary to discuss the distinction between knowledge of how to do something and knowledge about what one is doing. Perhaps the best way to proceed is by analogy. There are important differences between knowing how to drive a car, knowing how to fix a car, and knowing how to design a car, or, similarly, with understanding what goes on in a football game, being able to play football, and being able to describe the aerodynamics involved when a football is thrown or kicked. These differences carry over directly into language. We can understand and speak a language, we can edit and correct the language of others, and we can help to create a theory of language.

People are taught to understand much the way they are taught to drive a car. They see someone else do it, they themselves practice, and after they get the feel of it, off they go. You never have to know a thing about how your car runs, either in theory or in practice, to drive it competently (even magnificently). The knowledge that performers have of their performance ability is usually limited to being able to describe crudely what they are doing. They are rarely aware of exactly what they know; they just know how. They may even be able to teach the "how" that they know, because this can be done by imitation and correction. The theory need never be understood, and, indeed, if it is understood, it will usually in no way help the performance. Great musicians do not usually understand air flow, nor do they have well-developed theories of the physics of sound.

With reading it is much the same. Children learn to talk by imitation and correction. To teach reading and writing to a child capable of understanding and talking, it is necessary to give the information pertaining to reading and writing that the child does not as yet have. It follows that to teach writing, one must teach about the formation of letters, capitalization, punctuation, and other writing-specific phenomena.

Children's difficulty in reading often comes from a lack of confidence about guessing what is implicit in what they are reading. Teaching children to rely upon their prior knowledge is the crux of what needs to be taught. On the other hand, we do not want to teach children theories about the formal nature of that knowledge. An excellent example of a problem in this regard involves the teaching of grammar. These days instruction in grammar is usually part of a "language arts" curriculum. In our distinction between "knowing how" and "knowing what," it is clear that every child knows how to form a sentence. The most common definition of grammar states that grammar defines what is in a language. Since every child who speaks English is speaking English sentences, by this definition he can only be speaking grammatical sentences. To put this another way, the child has rules for putting a sentence together that he uses all the time. These rules constitute the "grammar" that he uses. It is obvious that, prior to entering school, most children who speak English have no idea what a noun is. But they do know all the rules that they will ever need for knowing how to manipulate nouns. "Noun" is part of the vocabulary of the language theorist, not the language user.

If grammatical rules in no way affect reading ability, what do they relate to? From a stylistic point of view, they relate to writing, but they do so only at a very advanced stage. Consider the rule "Do not use a preposition to end a sentence." In the first sentence of this paragraph, I violated that rule. English speakers regularly violate it, which could be seen to call into question its validity as a grammatical rule of English. Nevertheless, it is considered poor style to place prepositions at the end of sentences.

Making children aware of such rules is important, if they might need to know them. It is important to learn to write well. But writing well is something that must be learned considerably after one learns to read. Teaching grammatical notions to elementary-school children is simply premature. Furthermore, that kind of teaching may turn children off to school entirely.

With respect to grammar, then, a child who has never heard of nouns and verbs will be in no way handicapped. She will be able to read, and speak, with the best. We do not want to confuse a child who already knows how to use language by teaching her theories of language, which are at this point in a muddle. No theory has been shown to be correct as of this writing. Why teach children aspects of a theory of syntax that have never been proven and are in no way relevant to the development of skills that they will need?

The important point is that we must teach children those things that will help them in reading. Not everything that is currently part of the reading curriculum has relevance in aiding reading. A great many things that are taught are holdovers from outdated conceptions of the three R's. We most certainly do wish to make our children facile with language. But to do this requires that we first ensure that they are good readers. A child does not need to know the theoretical constructs of language in order to be able to use language effectively. What do we want to teach, then? The major issue is teaching reading comprehension.

Children can sound out or recognize words, many of which they may not really understand at all. They may appear to be reading, if what one counts as reading is the pronunciation of the words on the page. But comprehension is hardly indicated by whether a child can utter a string of words aloud. Try reading a foreign language that uses our alphabet—Italian or Spanish, for example. Can you "read" these languages? Since their pronunciations conform well to the way the languages are written, it is rather easy for an English speaker to become fairly competent in reading aloud. But what does this demonstrate? Certainly the ability bears no relationship at all to comprehension. A beginning reader is not unlike the English speaker who at first sight can read Italian aloud. Since an adult will want to comprehend what he is reading, teaching him to read Italian requires teaching him the meaning of the words, and that is also what the reading-comprehension process requires.

To assess the problem of what to teach in teaching comprehension, we must attempt to determine what is likely to prevent a child from comprehending a given text. Or, to put it more positively, what must a child know, beyond the issue of word recognition, in order to read a story? Let us consider an example and use it as a guide to the problem. The story I have chosen is from an edition of *Treasure Island* that is described as appropriate for children from eight to fourteen years of age. I will take seven passages and attempt to indicate the kind of trouble a child might have in reading those passages, and the source of trouble.

1. AWKWARD EXPRESSION

I remember . . . when the brown old seaman *took up his lodgings* at the Admiral Benbow.

One problem children have in reading stories is a lack of familiarity with certain idiomatic usage, or modes of expression. Here the problem is obvious because the expression "took up his lodgings" is an out-of-date phrase. The child may well know, or be able to figure out, what each word is, but he may still be confused.

2. SCRIPT INSTANTIATION

. . . lodgings at *the Admiral Benbow*

Adult readers now realize that the sailor has entered a kind of hotel (or inn, as we are later told). But how do we know that? We know it the same way we know that in "Sam ordered a pizza at Luigi's," "Luigi's" is a restaurant, probably an Italian restaurant.

3. PLAN ASSESSMENT

"This is a handy cove," the seaman said to my father, "and a well-placed inn. Do you have much company here?"

An adult reader will recognize that the seaman has a plan to stay at the inn if it is quiet and secluded enough. We assume he is hiding, or that perhaps something even more sinister is occurring. We await the reason why. But does a child? A child must be taught to look for the plans of the characters she meets. She must learn to question their motives and see the larger picture. This is a very difficult thing for a child to learn. It involves a very new point of view for her. Young children tend to accept the people they meet at face value. They trust everybody. Moreover, they accept the world as it is. They do not see or look for sinister plans or plots.

To some extent, movies can be an aid here. Children who watch

movies will learn something of plot development and sinister plans.
But there is a great difference between processing text and processing
pictures. In reading, many more inferences must be made about what
characters actually have done. In movies, actions are spelled out in
detail. Understanding that a character has a plan is facilitated by
watching a movie. Inferring the details of his plan is very easy when
watching a movie because we just watch the plan develop. We see
every detail of a character's actions. In reading a story, we assess the
plot, but we also must infer the details. Most plots depict in some way
the interaction and blocking of plans and the attempt to achieve goals.
Tracking such things in detail is often beyond a child's experience. She
must be taught to track plans.

4. Background Knowledge of Characters

> Though his clothes and manners were coarse, he did not seem to be an
> ordinary seaman. . . .

Would a child recognize an ordinary seaman from an extraordinary
one? What comparison is being made here? Without some knowledge
of what a seaman does, looks like, wants, and so on, it is difficult to
understand this sentence.

Two things are important here. First, a child should be given
stories for which he has the relevant background knowledge. Second,
a child must be taught to assess the traits of the characters he meets.
What kind of person is being talked about?

5. Plot Development

> One day he took me aside and promised me money if I would keep me
> eye open for a seafaring man with one leg.

The plot thickens. We know that, but how does a child assess it?
She must understand something of what a plot is, how stories develop,
and so on.

6. WORLD KNOWLEDGE

> His stories were what frightened people most of all. Our plain country people were as shocked by his language as they were by the crimes he described. My father believed that the inn would be ruined by the captain's tyranny; that people would stop coming because he sent them shivering to their beds.

To understand this passage, one needs to know something of the values and morals of an English town in the eighteenth century. Further, it is most important to know about businesses—inns, in particular—and how and why they run. A basic knowledge of commerce is needed here. This story can be understood effectively only in the presence of the appropriate background knowledge.

7. TRACKING PROPS AND GOALS

> "He's a bad one, but there's worse behind him. They're after my sea chest."

This line is the crux of the story so far. It indicates that there will be a fair amount of plot associated with the sea chest. Indeed, the content of the sea chest is the crucial issue in the story. How is the child to know this? How do we know it? We know it because we know about valuable objects, greed, likely containers for valuable objects, and story structure. When we see a particular prop in a story, we expect it to be used in the story. The child must be taught to look out for props and to track the goals associated with those props.

8. INFERENCES, BELIEFS, AND REASONING

> When I told my mother all I knew, she agreed we were in a difficult and dangerous position.

Why are they in a difficult position? The story makes it obvious. Our heroes possess objects of value that others know about and will want to steal. But this is not necessarily obvious to a child. A child must be taught to construct chains of reasoning based on beliefs derived from what he has heard so far and from what he knows of life. But what does the child know of life? Some of that kind of knowledge is taught by stories. Much of it must be taught when, or preferably before, a story is encountered. The child must learn to figure out what is going on.

The key point is that a child must have a well-developed sense of the world around him in order to understand stories about the world. This indicates that a great deal of what must be taught to enable reading is not so much language, per se. Rather, it is the acquisition of world knowledge, and the processes that utilize that knowledge, that constitute the key issues in reading comprehension. But how can we teach world knowledge? Should we even try? It is clear that we can enhance the child's ability to use what he already knows to help him read.

━━

Language and knowledge are intricately entwined. There is a tendency when reading is taught to teach language, but without the knowledge part of language. What is considered significant about language and about the teaching of language is the form of language, the grammar and spelling, but not the meaning.

To see how people go about dealing with meanings in their daily use of language, consider the sentence "John upset Mary." One of the first and most important things to realize is that this sentence is ambiguous. We can think of a number of different meanings:

John did something to cause Mary to be upset (or anxious).
John knocked Mary over.
John, who should have lost his match with Mary, won.

Yet we can rule out certain of them if we hear the sentence in context, preceded by other sentences. Early in our education, we learn that "upset" is a verb. (It is also a noun and an adjective. Since it functions as a verb in our sentence, if we ask the question "What is the action going on in the sentence?" we might expect that the answer should be "upsetting.")

This answer is inadequate if we require that an action be something that an actor do to something else. We can say, "John upset Mary," but we cannot really mean it. That is to say, upsetting is not something one can do to someone. Try to picture John in your mind upsetting Mary. What do you see? Whatever you see for this sense of "upset" is liable to be quite different from what someone else sees. Because the mental pictures one forms upon hearing a sentence are analogous to what one perceives to be the meaning of a sentence, we can say here that "John upset Mary" has a very imprecise meaning. The meaning of "upset" is quite unclear for the first sense of the word given above. The action denoted by "upset" is unknown. However, the meaning of the rest of the sentence is much clearer. Whatever this unknown action was, we know that the actor was John. Do we know what the object of that action was? The temptation is to say that we do, but the object is quite dependent on the particular action. We do know something about Mary, but not whether she was the object of John's action. For example, Mary may have heard about something John did to someone else, or to himself. Rather, all we know is that Mary was upset (in the sense of anxious) as a result of John's action.

One of the more important features of the meaning of the sentence that we have just shown is what it leaves out. We know that John did something. The fact that we do not know what he did is very important. It points out the imprecision of most speech. We are quite content to leave out the actual action performed by John and speak only about the action's consequences. In fact, English has a great many words like "upset." Nearly any word that describes the mental or physical state of a person can be used as a verb or has a verb-form equivalent. Thus, we can have: *John disturbed Mary, John angered Mary, John pleased Mary,* and so on. We recognize that there has been an action left out of these statements. We don't know what John actually did in any of these cases. What do we do about it? The answer is that we often fill in the missing action by relying upon what we know about the world to help us make a good guess about what is going on. The extraction of meaning from sentences is a kind of hit-or-miss process.

Most speech, then, leaves a great deal of room for misunderstanding. Because we are left to our own devices to guess what John did, we often guess wrong and then forget which part we actually heard and which part we guessed. We may even go on to relate an inaccurate message to the next person with whom we speak.

To tell more about the action that has been left out, we can use a "by" phrase. That is, we can say, "John upset Mary by yelling at her." This informs us of the action that was missing, and we can thus replace the "did something" with "John yelled at Mary" in our present representation.

As listeners we employ rules that allow us to decide how to combine concepts that are presented in a sentence. Sometimes these rules are the grammatical rules of English, but often they are not. A sentence such as *I saw a building walking down the street* is understandable in two possible ways. However, a hearer is much more apt to assume that the speaker was walking down a street and passed a building than that a building was actually walking down the street, because we know rules of the world that tell us which possibility is more likely. Our job is not to rule out possibilities but to choose between them. Our preferences in ambiguous situations are based on what we know about the world.

In fact, understanding often means explicitly rejecting as a possibility what a sentence seems to be saying because we know better. For example, *The rock hit the boy* is a sentence that really needs to be interpreted. This sentence has an inanimate subject that seems to be doing things. A sentence such as *The rock hit the boy* is understood very differently from *The man hit the boy*. We recognize that rocks never really act. We do not for a minute imagine that the rock decided to do anything. Rather, we recognize immediately that rocks are inanimate, and that ordinarily they function as objects of an action. Conceptually, then, the rock in this sentence must be an object of someone or something else's action. "What role does the boy play?" and "Who is the actor?" are two important questions to ask here. We must also concern ourselves with determining what the action in this event is. Let us think about the event a bit. What really must have happened? For a rock to have hit a boy, the rock must have been in motion. Since rocks cannot put themselves in motion, something must have put the rock in motion. Three choices seem possible: (1) a person or an animal; (2) a natural force, such as the wind, the ocean, or an earthquake; or (3) a machine.

The next question is: "Done what?" We really do not know what action set the rock in motion; it could have been pushed, swung, or thrown. We do know that the action we are concerned with is not "hit," as found in our sentence. (True, the rock may have been hit to have been set in motion, but the rock itself did no such action. When a rock is set in motion by an actor, a contact between the actor and the rock has taken place.)

Language can be highly ambiguous and imprecise. People know what they think they have heard (even though it may not correspond to what the speaker wanted them to have understood). Understanding means determining what really happened. We have had to decide on the particular meaning of the highly ambiguous word that was used, "hit." What do we know, then? It is very important to note that a lack of concrete information at any point in the understanding process is itself information. The fact that we do not know what action took place means that we may need to discover it somewhere else in the understanding process. To do this, we need to know what it is that we do not know. Since it is not possible to remedy a lack of information without recognizing that such a lack exists, the very knowledge of the lack is itself useful information.

The key to understanding is the knowledge of the nature of events. The understanding of language is a process whereby a person decodes a sentence, either read or heard, into a set of concepts that is consonant with the knowledge of the world that he or she has and that expresses the meaning of what was read. One must make inferences to find out what is true apart from what is just literally read.

The key issue in comprehension, we have seen, is the application of appropriate knowledge to a situation. Such knowledge helps to fill in the details behind that situation. Children cannot be expected to understand stories about which they lack background knowledge.

But children can be taught to expand their background knowledge and, thus, what they can read.

The process of understanding stories relies heavily on our ability to extract what is implicitly true in a story or sequence of events. Think about what you are doing when you attempt to understand the following:

> John was hungry. He went into Goldstein's and ordered a pastrami sandwich. It was served to him quickly. He left the waitress a large tip.

Suppose that after reading this, you were asked the following questions. How many of them would you have trouble answering?

> What is Goldstein's?
> What did John eat?
> Who made the sandwich?
> Who took John's order?
> Who served the sandwich?
> Why did John leave a large tip?

For the most part they are easy and have obvious answers. Any reading-comprehension test that contained such a story would be considered simple. But at no point are we told explicitly that Goldstein's is a restaurant (and probably a Jewish delicatessen), that John ate anything at all (let alone the pastrami sandwich), or that the waitress brought the sandwich to John.

What enables people to understand stories such as the preceding one is knowledge that is organized into structures we call scripts. Scripts organize all the information we have in memory about how a commonplace occurrence (such as going to a restaurant) usually takes place. In addition, scripts point out what behavior is appropriate for a particular situation. Knowing that you are in a restaurant script leads to knowing that if you ask a waitress for food, she is likely to bring it. On the other hand, we know that if you ask her for a pair of shoes, or if you ask her for food while she is returning home on a bus, she is likely to react as if you had done something odd.

We use our knowledge of everyday situations to help us understand stories or discourse about those situations. We need not ask why somebody wants to see our ticket when we enter a theater, or why we should be quiet, or how long it is appropriate to sit in our seat. Knowledge of specific situations, such as theater-going, allows us to interpret the remarks that people make about theaters. Consider how difficult it would be to interpret "Second aisle on your right" without the detailed knowledge about theaters that the patron and the usher share. It would be rather odd to respond "What about the second aisle on my right?" or "Where is my seat?" or "Is this how I get into the theater?" The usher simply takes the ticket and, assuming you understand and have knowledge about theaters, utters this otherwise cryptic remark without your saying anything.

We often leave out the obvious connections in a story. We do this as speakers because we assume that the hearer has a script available that will make things sensible. If such a script is not available, however, the hearer (or reader) will be confused. Look at the following two stories:

> John went to a restaurant. He asked the waitress for the house special. He paid the check and left.

> John went to a park. He asked the midget for a mouse. He picked up the box and left.

In the second story we are unprepared for the reference to "the" midget rather than "a" midget and "the" box rather than "a" box. We also cannot figure out what the mouse and the box have to do with each other. The story does not refer to a standard situation; we know of none that relates midgets, mouses, boxes, and parks. The story is thus not comprehensible, because we have no world knowledge that helps us to connect the parts. If there were a standard "mouse-buying script" in which midgets in parks sold mice that were always packed in boxes, then we would be able to apply the script and connect the elements of the story.

What scripts do, then, is provide "connectivity." In the first story, which is superficially quite similar to the second, there is a great deal of connectivity. We are not surprised when "the" waitress or "the" check are mentioned. We understand exactly the relationship between asking for the house special and paying the check. We also assume that John ate the food he was served, that he waited a while before being served, that he may have looked at a menu, and so on. All this information is brought up by the restaurant script.

Not all stories are script-dominated. That is, understanding what script one is in is useful only for setting the context. The point at which scripts cease to help is the point at which the unexpected (and thus the interesting) begins.

What scripts does a first- or second-grader know? Since scripts are cultural indicators of the purest kind, the question cannot be answered universally. It cannot even be answered for the United States. There exist many subcultures in the United States. No one reading text will suffice for all regions of the country, since few regions, and few social strata within a region, share the same script. Farmers' children, for example, will know the "working chores of the farm" script. City children will know the "playing ball in the street" script. Suburban children will know the "going shopping at the mall" script. A story about school buses requires knowledge that children who walk to school may not have. A story on zoos may be lost to children in rural areas. One on planes is lost to poor children, and one on farms to city children.

If we expect children to understand what they read, they must possess the script that the materials they are reading relies upon. Either we use the scripts that they already know in the stories we ask them to read, or we teach them new scripts. We can, of course, do both. The emphasis ought not to be on teaching reading at all, but on teaching knowledge. Reading is, in essence, a simple task. It is no more difficult than following a movie. The difficult part in following a movie is trying to make sense of a character's actions when one has had no experience with that particular kind of actor or those kinds of actions. The concept of planning to achieve a goal, whether by stereotypical plans like scripts or by novel planning techniques, must be taught to children before serious reading can or ought to be taught.

To teach children to track plans while reading, we must address ourselves to three issues:

1. Teaching children to follow stories that involve plans and goals
2. Teaching children how to plan to achieve a goal
3. Teaching children about goal conflicts, resolutions, and other aspects of stories

In the context of reading, the first step is to accustom children to reading stories in which the relationship between sentences in the text is one of plan to goal:

A. Johnny was very hungry. He opened a cookbook.
B. Johnny was very hungry. He opened the cupboard.
C. Johnny was very hungry. He got on his bicycle.
D. Johnny was very hungry. He lit the oven.
E. Johnny was very hungry. He called to his mother.
F. Johnny was very hungry. He got some money from his piggy bank.

What is being taught here are goal-plan relationships. The relationships inherent in these sentences are as follows:

A. *Gaining knowledge.* To achieve a goal, it is sometimes necessary to have more knowledge about how to achieve it. This is the relationship of cookbook to hunger.

B. *Enablements.* Often gaining control of an object requires doing something that might otherwise be seen as irrelevant. Here opening the cupboard is relevant if we assume that the cupboard contains food. This opening enables the "gain control" plan to operate.

C. *Gaining proximity.* To satisfy a goal, it is often necessary to move to where the satisfaction can take place. Here we must assume that Johnny is going to some kind of eating place.

D. *Preparation.* Even when all elements are present (when we know what to do, have control of the goal objects, and are in the right place), certain preparatory steps must be taken. Here lighting the oven is part of that preparatory procedure.

E. *Getting an agent.* We need not do everything for ourselves. Sometimes others will do it for us. Of course, they are only assistants in a plan; ultimately, we will have to eat for ourselves.

F. *Planning ahead.* Often a plan involves multiple steps. Going to a restaurant without taking money or knowing how to get there can be a problem. Here Johnny is planning ahead for a goal that we can guess (eating ice cream?).

Quite often children don't plan, however. Usually they have a script available to help them through a situation. This is most likely to be true in common situations—when one is hungry, for example. The best way to explain sentences that indicate steps in a plan is to use stories that involve novel situations. Teaching ought to introduce the attempt to make children figure things out on their own. In this context, then, the questions that should be asked of children about the preceding stories include:

1. Why did Johnny do what he did?
2. What else could he have done?
3. How well did his actions help him get what he wants?
4. What will he do next?

I am not suggesting that the theoretical elements be taught explicitly. It makes no more sense to teach a theory of the construction of plans than it does to teach a theory of grammar. Children should not be asked to underline enablements or categorize actions in terms of planning. Knowing how to use such information, not knowing the information explicitly, is what is important here. If the child can answer the above questions, he has understood.

The next stage in reading stories based on plans and goals is helping the child to recognize that actions can enable one to put a plan into effect or to reach a goal. Here are some examples:

Johnny wanted a new baseball glove. When Johnny's father got home, Johnny greeted him at the door with a big hug. Then he asked his father if he wanted to play catch.

Why did Johnny greet his father in the way he did?
Why do you think Johnny wanted to play catch?
What do you think will happen when they play catch?
What would you do if you wanted a new baseball glove?

Susie was jumping rope with Jane. She was tired and she wanted to quit. But Jane hadn't had her turn yet. Suddenly, Susie yelled that her ankle hurt.

Why couldn't Susie quit?
Did Susie's ankle really hurt?
Why did she say it did?
How do you think Jane will feel?
What kind of person is Susie?

In each of these stories, a child has a goal. In both cases the goals are stated and obvious. Children must learn to see how someone can plan a course of action to achieve a goal. In neither of these stories do the children take the most direct course of action. Children must be taught to recognize the course of action, or plan, that is being followed.

Once we find that a character has acted dishonestly, we can expect him to do so again. The following is taken from the *Treasure Island* story used earlier:

Silver went over to talk with the pirates. They laughed together. Then he saw Jim. Jim asked who the men were that Silver had laughed with. Silver said, "What men?"

Such stories provide good opportunities to discuss issues such as guilt by association, bad traits, and so on. In stories, we are rarely told something that isn't intended to set up something else. Children must be taught to look for these clues in life, not just in texts, to guide them in their predictions about actions and their consequences.

As readers, we learn to figure out what goal is being pursued.

Jane left the house quietly. She had all her money with her. At last she was at the store. She went in. It was a store that sold pipes. But they were all so expensive.

What is Jane planning on doing?
Why do you think she is doing that?
What is the difficulty she has in achieving her goal?
What can she do about it?

It is often a good idea to have the child answer questions like those above, and then to proceed to the rest of the story. It could continue:

How was she going to get her father his birthday present? Then she thought that her older sister might help. She hurried home.

Understanding means learning to figure out why people do what they do. Children must learn to recognize that a story can mislead them; they can make a wrong guess and still recover.

In real life, there are times when we want what someone else also wants. Many children's stories are based on goal competition and the means of achieving a compromise or outright success. The following is from Aesop:

Once upon a time, there was a dishonest Fox who lived in a cave, and a vain and trusting Crow who lived in an elm tree. The Crow had gotten a piece of cheese and was holding it in his mouth. One day, the Fox walked from his cave, across the meadow, to the elm tree. He saw the Crow and the cheese and became hungry. He decided that he might get the cheese if the Crow spoke, so he told the Crow that he liked his singing very much and wanted to hear him sing. The Crow was very pleased with the Fox's request and began to sing. The cheese fell out of his mouth, down to the ground. The Fox picked up the cheese and told the Crow that he was stupid. The Crow was angry and didn't trust the Fox anymore. The Fox returned to his cave.

What did the Fox want?
What did the Crow want?
Why did the Fox ask the Crow to sing?
Why did the Crow sing?
Who won?
What would you have done if you were the Fox?
What would you have done if you were the Crow?

Here we have a series of plans and counterplans, all carried out in pursuit of the same goal. How easy is it to understand this story if you have never tried to achieve such goals yourself?

The purpose in systematically teaching children about goals and plans is to lead them to make the appropriate assumptions, create the right expectations, draw sensible conclusions, and otherwise tie together what they have read. Many of the questions I have proposed here are currently being asked of children in reading-comprehension instruction. But for the most part they are being asked randomly and unsystematically. Thus, although a child might occasionally have to speculate on some aspect of what he has read, he is not systematically learning to ask these kinds of questions of himself. And that is what he must do if he is to learn to understand.

I have attempted here to present reading as being not wholly different from other cognitive processes. If you can't read, you probably can't think, either, not because reading helps one think, but because reading entails thinking. It seems to me that the emphasis on reading instruction in this country is misplaced. To teach reading, give a child books to read, not lessons on prefixes and suffixes. To teach the thinking that reading entails, some kind of instruction is necessary. Children must be taught to reason in an inquisitive fashion, and that requires that schools encourage such behavior.

At the onset of reading, the typical child functions effectively with her language. Often the teaching of reading is confused with teaching a child about her language. Reading may be a new subject for the child, but comprehension is not. To teach a child to read requires concentrating on the problems in reading that are specific to reading. These are, for the most part, simple and straightforward and can be dispensed with after the first grade. The most significant of these problems are the association of sounds with printed words and the reliance on prediction and memory in the sight recognition of words.

The making of inferences to add facts to those explicitly mentioned and the understanding of the role of actions and characters in a story are skills critical to reading; but they are by no means specific to reading. They can, and should, be taught elsewhere. I have suggested that the movies are a good place to start. Why? Because going to the movies is fun, and good movies stimulate one's curiosity.

Of course, it should be clear what the goal is here. The goal is not to teach reading at all. It is to teach children to be able to gather information and be critical in their understanding of that information. Naturally, books are excellent sources of new information. But in the computer age they are by no means the only source. The goal is thinking, questioning, analysis, and synthesis, not reading.

How do children learn to speak well? If they are not to be instructed in their language as part of reading, should they be instructed in their language at all? The answer is complex. There is no need to instruct elementary-school children in their language. They know, and will continue to learn, how to speak and understand, and the fine points of syntax and semantics. This knowledge develops by usage, not by explicit instruction. Thus, it should be "taught" by placing children in situations that involve speaking. This is what is done by parents. And it is what must be done by the teacher.

My suggestions are these: Have conversations with children in class. They should have to listen critically to what the teacher says. After they can read a little, have them talk about what they read and hear. We teach children to use language by making them use it. The more they use it, the more facile they will become with it. Children learn language by imitation and use. Give them good models. Do not instruct them explicitly in the use of nouns, predicates, and antonyms, and in other aspects of language that they implicitly know.

The study of language has been the focus of my professional life. I believe that the study of language—how it works, its history and development—would be a useful part of any high-school student's curriculum. Such a subject should be taught in high school, but not because it will teach the student to speak, write, or read better. It will not. Rather, it should be taught because an educated person should have knowledge of language.

Written language makes up a comparatively small part of most of our lives. Even the most educated of people spend more time speaking and hearing than reading or writing. Children understand only a small portion of what they hear. Yet they push on. Eventually, when they are ready to pay attention to a new word, they can ask about it or figure out what it means. But this happens only with a comparatively small percentage of the new words that they encounter. The same is true of reading. When a child discovers a new word in the course of reading, he usually finds it much easier to skip it than to learn its meaning. When the child completely understands the context that surrounds a word, in the sense of having predicted its meaning, he can then learn the word by reading it. On the other hand, when a new word is spoken by a friend or teacher, used a second or third time, and finally used by the child himself, it will be possible to learn the word. This is a key point. A combination of reading and usage will result in the learning of new vocabulary. But the child must be encouraged to use the new word and respond to others using it.

Can we teach new vocabulary in school? I believe we can and must. The "how" of the matter is crucial.

━━━

The watchword throughout this essay has been *knowledge*. The acquisition of knowledge about the world is the single most important part of reading. You cannot read about that which makes no sense to you. To prove this point to yourself, try reading a folktale, in English, taken from a culture very far removed from yours. A classic in this regard is "The War of the Ghosts," an Eskimo folktale. Psychologists have demonstrated that this particular story is very hard for most Americans to remember and read, as are all stories for which one does not possess the appropriate background knowledge.

> One night two young men from Egulac went down to the river to hunt seals, and while they were there it became foggy and calm. Then they heard war cries, and they thought, *Maybe this is a war party.* They escaped to the shore and hid behind a log. Now canoes came up, and they heard the noise of paddles, and saw one canoe coming up to them.
>
> There were five men in the canoe, and they said, "What do you think? We wish to take you along. We are going up the river to make war on the people."

One of the young men said, "I have no arrows. I will not go along. I might be killed. My relatives do not know where I have gone. But you," he said, turning to the other, "may go with them."

So one of the young men went, but the other returned home.

And the warriors went up the river to a town on the other side of Kalama. The people came down to the water, and they began to fight, and many were killed. But presently the young man heard one of the warriors say, "Quick, let us go home; that Indian has been hit."

Now he thought, *Oh, they are ghosts.* He did not feel sick, but they said he had been shot.

So the canoes went back to Egulac, and the young man went ashore to his house, and made a fire. And he told everybody and said, "Behold, I accompanied the ghosts, and we went to fight. Many of our fellows were killed, and many of those who attacked us were killed. They said I was hit, and I did not feel sick."

He told it all, and then he became quiet. When the sun rose he fell down. Something black came out of his mouth. His face became contorted. The people jumped up and cried.

He was dead.

The story is understandable if you "know" certain Eskimo "facts," such as: When people die, their souls, which are black, come out of their mouths. When ghosts shoot you, you do not feel it. Without these facts, the story is quite confusing.

Children face a similar situation in reading. They need to have background facts at hand, and to fill them in, so as to connect the sentences. But there is a paradox here. We use knowledge in order to read, but don't we read in order to gain knowledge? Isn't that one of the main reasons for teaching children to read?

I have attempted to treat this paradox within the progression of stages given earlier. After children learn how to fill in the implicit details of a story, and to track characters' goals and plans, they are prepared to acquire knowledge via reading. In other words, the basic background knowledge that they possess is used to help them learn to read stories that track plans and goals. The general knowledge of why people do things and how they do them can then be used to help gain knowledge about different goals and plans that are unfamiliar to them. After plans, goals, and scripts have been thoroughly learned, as they apply to reading, children must be taught to reason, draw analogies, relate one experience to another, and assess what is happening in a situation and why it is happening.

A child who can learn the language of science, and who has familiarity with its methods, can also read about science. I once brought my four-year-old son to an undergraduate class I was teaching. He happened to notice the computer terminal in the room and began to talk about how he was going to "log on," when to do a "control C," or an "SYS," how to "run a program," and so on. The students in the class were astounded. But there was nothing astounding about it. As the son of a professor of computer science, he knew all about computer terminals and had picked up the appropriate terminology from his attempts to acquire a working knowledge of how to use them. I did not present him with an elementary-school-level computer programming text. But he would have been capable of reading such a text. And that is exactly the point.

A child who sees a simple experiment in chemistry conducted in front of him, assuming his interest is excited by a good presentation, will quickly learn such words as "experiment," "procedure," "method," "instruments," "chemical," and so on. If he is allowed to participate directly in experiments, he will learn these words that much better. If this kind of firsthand experience happens frequently, then the words describing the experiment will become second nature to him. This is how to "teach" new vocabulary.

Reading is not just reading per se. It is knowledge gathering, it is entertainment, it is inquiry, it is analysis. To acquire knowledge, one must have knowledge. The reason Johnny can't read and the reason his old man won't read is that neither of them knows much, and they don't want to know much. Teach them about something that interests them, teach them to be interested in more things, and reading will follow. As long as a child cares about what he is reading, he will happily read—if he has the requisite background knowledge. How do we get him to care about *reading*? We get him to care about *knowing* first.

In Defense of Elitism

GERALD FEINBERG

The arguments for doing some things as well as possible are spiritual as well as pragmatic. Whatever the original reason was for doing certain activities, their continued successful performance helps to define the character of any society. One can plausibly say that what a society holds most sacred is defined by those activities that it insists be done as well as possible.

elitism—*the leadership by the choice part or segment*

In what passes for social commentary in present-day America, it is hard to find anyone who has anything favorable to say about elitism. Many writers regard it as an unanswerably devastating criticism of an institution or of a course of action to describe it as elitist. This nearly unanimous agreement on the social undesirability of elitism is unaccompanied by any sustained analysis that warrants the conclusion that elitism is universally undesirable. Indeed, an examination of some of our hallowed institutions shows that elitism is fully accepted in some circumstances, even though no one calls attention to it in those terms. No voices have been raised to condemn the Los Angeles Lakers basketball team or the Chicago Symphony Orchestra, even though those institutions are elitist according to any plausible definition of that term.

However, elitism has been attacked in many circumstances—for example, by those who object to the geographical distribution of federal scientific research grants, and the composition of the student bodies of schools like the Bronx High School of Science, whose purpose is the training of those with high ability in specific activities. A variety of criticisms has been leveled at the practice of using merit as the sole criterion in determining which universities should be given federal grants to carry out scientific research, or who should attend such schools. In many cases, including the two that I have mentioned, the criticisms have succeeded in changing the previous practice so that merit is no longer the sole criterion. These changes have been to the detriment of the institutions, and of many of their members. In the fear of being branded as elitist, we have lowered the quality of institutions devoted to socially worthwhile purposes, and by so doing, we have sacrificed both important aims of society and the welfare of some of the most talented among us.

73

Not only is elitism tacitly accepted in some aspects of American life, but a convincing intellectual case can be made for it, both in those places where it is unquestionably accepted and in the places where it has been under attack, such as the composition of the faculties of major universities. I will show why elitist institutions, those who choose their members on the basis of merit, are an essential means for carrying out some of the activities that we jointly consider most worthwhile. I will focus on elitist universities, such as M.I.T., and on the schools that prepare students for them. This is where most of my own experience lies, and where I have seen the follies of anti-elitism most directly. But many of my arguments would also apply elsewhere, to elite musical or athletic institutions.

I am not arguing that elitism is a desirable approach to determining who should govern society. I agree with the view that was adopted early in our society that participation in the process of government by a large part of society is a more important matter than how effective the governors are.

My defense of the proposition that elitism is a desirable attitude, at least in certain situations, is based on two simple ideas. One is that some activities are accepted as so worthwhile, both by those that do them and by society at large, that they should be done as well as they can be done. The other proposition is that some individuals are much better at doing these activities than others are, or can become by any methods now known. I will first give the arguments for these propositions, then show why they make a strong case for elitism.

There is a list of activities that any society considers to be intrinsically worthwhile. The list is usually not spelled out anywhere, but it can be inferred from the ways in which the society spends its financial and human resources. Some of these worthwhile activities, such as winning a tennis match or painting a picture, mainly involve individuals. Where these individual activities are concerned, the issue of elitism is rarely raised directly. For the most part, there is little serious argument about the positive role of elitism in individual activities, and for that reason I will not discuss that issue further in this article.

There are others among the list of worthwhile activities that are performed by groups and often require ongoing institutions through which they are carried out. In modern American society, the list of worthwhile group activities would include such diverse pursuits as musical performances, both by symphony orchestras and rock groups; team sports, such as major-league baseball; and scientific research, which is mostly now done by groups of substantial size. Sometimes, as with symphony orchestras, the groups are absolutely necessary to carry out the activities. In other cases, as with universities consisting of diverse faculties, it might be possible to do the same activities through other institutional arrangements, but the existing institutions appear to work well, and there is no reason to think that other arrangements would be more effective.

The reasons for valuing activities are, of course, varied. Furthermore, those participating in the activities often value them for reasons that differ from those of spectators or consumers. For example, scientific research is valued by many scientists mainly for the insights it gives them into the workings of the universe, while many nonscientists value it mainly for its technological by-products. Such differences in emphasis sometimes lead to disagreements over priorities, in scientific research and elsewhere. Nevertheless, it seems likely that there would be fairly general agreement on a list of group activities that our society considers worthwhile.

There might be more disagreement about the question of how important it is to perform these activities as well as possible. On this question, the main difference is likely to be between the views of people for whom the activity is peripheral and of those for whom it is central. People who are not especially interested in football might consider it an activity that can be tolerated but not consider it an important matter how well the game is played. But serious football fans would be appalled at a suggestion that the existing teams could be replaced without serious loss by players of lower ability. An illustration of this attitude occurred in 1987 during the strike of N.F.L. players. During three weeks, when the striking players were replaced by a group of substitutes, attendance at the games decreased considerably. For other activities, especially those affecting people's well-being, there is almost universal acceptance of the view that the activities should be done as well as possible. This acceptance exists both among those performing the activity and those benefiting from its results. For example, it has never to my knowledge been argued either by scientists or nonscientists that scientific research should be carried out by people who are less able than the best who can be found to do it.

The arguments for doing some things as well as possible are spiritual as well as pragmatic. Whatever the original reason was for doing certain activities, their continued successful performance helps to define the character of any society. One can plausibly say that what any society holds most sacred is defined by those activities that it insists be done as well as possible. In Periclean Athens, there were competitions for the best dramas, and the entries were performed for the whole population each year at religious festivals. In Renaissance Florence, artists competed for the right to design public monuments, and the winner was called upon to execute his proposal. In present-day America, scientists compete for public funds to carry out their experimental investigations, and the winners get to do the experiments. In none of these cases did the system work perfectly to reward merit. Yet, in each case, it succeeded in eliciting a very high level of achievement in the chosen field. The very existence of such competitions implies that each society valued the activity enough to require that those who were best at it should be those called upon to do it. It is not accidental that these societies all attained extremely high levels of achievement at the activities that they valued so highly. In America today there are a number of group activities that we value highly, as indicated by the amount of our resources that we devote to them. Usually, as in the case of scientific research, these are the activities in which our achievements are greatest. If we use criteria in choosing those who perform those activities other than that of producing the most able performance, we sacrifice something truly distinctive about our society.

In order to avoid this, we should arrange that the members of the institutions through which these worthwhile group activities are carried out are as able as possible. Making such choices of personnel assumes that some individuals are better than others at each such activity. This proposition would be regarded as obviously true by most people, but since it is a question of fact, such agreement does not necessarily make it so. So what is the evidence for the claim that some individuals are inevitably more able than others at certain activities? There can be no doubt that when actual performances are measured, there are differences in accomplishment. Some runners consistently achieve faster times for the one hundred–meter dash than others. Some painters consistently produce paintings more to the liking of art collectors and critics than others. Some scientists solve problems that other scientists have failed to solve. We do not all perform the same tasks at the same level. The level of performance cannot be so easily compared for all worthwhile human activities. How does one tell who is better among two sets of parents? But the fact that such comparisons cannot always be made should not cancel out the obvious fact that they can easily be made in many cases.

Furthermore, there are directly measurable differences in the elementary physical and mental abilities that enter into the performance of any complex activity. The measured level of such qualities as muscular strength, ability to distinguish between musical tones, or facility of word memorization all vary considerably within the population. While the precise relation between these elementary abilities and successful performance of complex tasks varies from activity to activity, such relations surely exist. Someone with low muscular strength is unlikely to be a successful shotputter, however good his technique. A person who is color blind will probably not be a successful painter.

It is true that not all differences in the level of performance of complex activities are the result of intrinsic differences in ability among the individuals being compared. Performance levels also depend on the degree of training that the individual has received, and on his or her motivation to succeed, to mention just two relevant factors. For example, impressive athletic performances have been achieved by people, such as Wilma Rudolph, who had disabilities that one might have thought would make it impossible for them to compete successfully with other athletes. Beethoven composed some of his greatest works while unable to hear them played.

Some scientists, such as psychologist B. F. Skinner and population biologist Richard Lewontin, have argued that any effect on performance due to intrinsic differences of ability among people is negligible, and that with proper training, any person can achieve what anyone else can achieve. Furthermore, in much of educational philosophy, there is an unconscious bias toward the position that, with ideal training, everyone would end up with the same performance.

Evidence for these views, at least as applied to humans, is lacking. Some animals have been trained, through the methods pioneered by Skinner, to perform activities that could not have been a part of their natural lives, such as a pigeon that was taught to play table tennis. However, this does not prove that it is possible, by means such as suitable positive reinforcement in early childhood, to train every human to perform any activity at a very high level. Such outstanding talents as Mozart, John Stuart Mill, and Norbert Weiner have been produced in this way. But it is difficult to separate the roles of heredity and training in these cases. Those three people came from families in which previous generations also had high levels of ability. Many parents have tried to imitate the achievements of the elders Mozart, Mill, or Weiner with their children and found that the effort was unsuccessful. If early training is all that is needed to produce a Mozart, then we must admit that the precise methods for such training still elude us. There are successful training programs to enhance specific abilities, such as memorization, but even these do not appear to enable everyone to reach the high levels that some people do spontaneously. We should systematically investigate the extent to which training and the stimulation of motivation can lead to high levels of performance of various activities by a randomly selected population. Until the data from such an investigation are forthcoming, one must regard the view that anyone can be trained to do anything as no more than an ideological prejudice.

In any case, even if the possibility can be realized of training anyone to do anything, this is relevant only for the future. Institutions must currently find their personnel among the existing population, who have not been subjected to hypothetical training programs that could enhance the performance of those without natural talent.

There is surely a hierarchy of performance abilities in the existing population, whatever the source of these abilities. Even the most zealous advocates of training do not maintain that any methods exist by which one could take adults and train them to perform at the highest levels in activities for which they are not naturally able. Nor do we have any methods by which motivation can be consistently made to substitute for high ability. Furthermore, it seems at least probable that whatever training methods are used will be more effective for those with natural ability than those without it. Therefore, in deciding who should belong to institutions that strive for a high level of achievement, there is currently no alternative to taking the abilities of the candidates as they occur and choosing among the candidates on the basis of these abilities. I will address later a different question—How should we go about training young people who have ability to perform at high levels in different activities?

It follows from my two main propositions that for those institutions devoted to carrying out worthy activities, the principal criterion that should be used to determine who belongs to them is a likely ability to contribute to the successful performance of the main activities of the institution. The use of other criteria that lead to membership in the institution by less able people, even for such purposes as the redressing of social inequities, will result in a lower level of performance of the worthy activities that are the institution's function. When society, because of other criteria that it imposes, insists that an institution employ less able people, this amounts to a decision that success in carrying out the worthwhile activity of the institution is less important than some other aim that will be furthered by such employment. Such a decision should not be accepted without strong objection on the part of those who value the basic function of these institutions.

How should the members of the institutions that carry out the most worthwhile functions be chosen? It is implicit in my argument that it is possible to predict in advance of their employment those people who are most able to perform the worthwhile functions. For most of the activities that I have in mind, a preliminary screening of possible candidates is not difficult. By the time someone is a plausible candidate for membership in the Boston Symphony Orchestra, the Princeton mathematics department, or the Chicago Bears football team, he or she will have already demonstrated a high degree of competence, through achievement in the relevant field. Of course, there will usually be many competent candidates for any position in such institutions. The criteria by which the apparently most competent candidates can be chosen are not always precise, and not the same from one type of institution to another.

A system that is generally used to select faculty at elitist universities is a form of apprenticeship, in which candidates are chosen provisionally and given the opportunity to prove their ability through actual performance. At universities, the apprentices are usually called assistant professors, and they are given five to seven years to demonstrate their abilities. Those who perform best during this apprenticeship are then chosen as permanent members of the institution. This system has for the most part been effective at staffing these universities with able faculty members. However, it does not work perfectly for several reasons. Criteria other than able performance in teaching and research may become involved in the decisions. Furthermore, even clearly able candidates may not be chosen at a given university because no permanent positions are available there at the time when a decision must be made about them. Most universities are partly or completely dependent financially on agencies outside themselves. For example, many universities are financed in whole or part by federal or local governments. The size of university faculties is, therefore, not completely under the control of the universities.

Even for an institution of fixed size, it would be possible to use a system in which new members, when they are judged to be more able, simply replace present members. This system is used by athletic teams, for example, where a player past his prime is usually sent away, unless he is fortunate enough to have a long-term contract. Universities generally do not follow this procedure, because of a practice known as tenure. The permanent faculties of universities have what are in effect lifetime jobs, and they cannot be replaced, except in very rare circumstances, even if obviously more able candidates for their positions are available. On its face, this tenure system seems like a clear violation of the principle of maximizing the performance of the functions of the university. To the extent that tenure for the present faculty interferes with the appointment of more qualified new faculty, universities are not using the people who can best perform the scholarly functions of research and teaching. It would be more in the spirit of maximizing high achievement to give university faculty members short-term contracts, somewhat like baseball players used to have, and to replace them with other, presumably younger, faculty members when their scholarly performance begins to wane. Of course, this could produce difficulties in finding new employment for the faculty members being replaced, but the force of argument I have been making is that the successful performance of the functions of elitist institutions should take precedence over the welfare of specific individuals.

However, there are some things to be said for the tenure system even within the context of elitism. College faculty members are not evaluated solely on the basis of performance. Tenure provides some security against those inside and outside of universities who would evaluate faculty on ideological grounds unrelated to the able performance of their functions. Tenure also acts as an inertial flywheel, which keeps faculties from changing very rapidly in response to intellectual fads. The security that tenure provides allows faculty to follow the lines of investigation that they consider important for extended periods of time even when these are not showing any immediate results. It has often happened that such investigations have ultimately proven to be immensely fruitful for science or scholarship. Finally, no university can always attract whomever it wants to its faculty. Other universities, and other centers of research, such as industrial laboratories, often seem more attractive to young scientists—for financial reasons or because better facilities are available there. In this situation, the added benefit of lifelong tenure may play an important role in attracting able young researchers to university faculties. Similar considerations apply in some of the social sciences, such as economics.

The tenure system must ultimately be evaluated in the light of whether there is an alternative to it that would result in better performance of the functions of universities. At present there is no clear evidence about whether the use of tenure has a significant effect in either direction on how well university faculty perform their research and teaching functions. There have been periods, such as the 1970s, in which many highly qualified people could not be appointed to university faculties because most of the available positions were already occupied by tenured faculty. However, this is not the usual situation. My experience is that at the physics departments of leading universities, the most able candidates for faculty positions have been able to obtain appointments, even in periods when few positions were available.

In view of the positive and negative aspects of university tenure in the context of elitism, it might be interesting for some universities to try to operate outside the tenure system, with the rapid turnover of faculty that this change would allow, in order to see the effect of this change on the faculty that could be appointed and on the relative performance of this faculty.

An alternative system for choosing the members of institutions would be to give nationwide examinations to test performance in some field and award positions on the basis of performance on these examinations. While this method has been used in some European countries to choose professors at universities, it has not been used much in America to determine membership in elitist institutions, although it is sometimes used to decide which candidates will enter the training programs for these institutions. The elitist institutions in America, especially the universities, are usually independent of one another and of the central government. Therefore, even if a rank ordering of candidates could be determined, no mechanism exists for assigning these candidates among those institutions that have positions to fill. Furthermore, such examinations are not yet sufficiently accurate predictors of performance that they can effectively be used to determine membership in elitist institutions. For example, tests such as the

Graduate Record Examination, given to college seniors, correlate only moderately well with performance in graduate school and even less well with eventual research or scholarly achievements.

Many universities allow the present members of their faculties to choose new members, with only moderate intervention by those outside the faculty. This system usually works well to ensure the quality of new appointments. Most faculty members wish to have colleagues who are as able as can be obtained. However, there have been serious problems with the system in a variety of circumstances. One problem that has occurred at some universities is disagreement among present faculty members about what constitutes merit on the part of prospective members of the institution. Such disagreements occur not so much over the merits of individual candidates as over the propriety of the work that they do. Often this problem exists because of fundamental disagreements among present faculty members about what aspects of their field are most important or significant. This type of conflict is likely to arise in one of two circumstances. If there has been a substantial change in the nature of the field itself, then there can be "generational" conflicts between those who practice the old and new versions. For example, in several recent situations at universities, conflicts have occurred between those who practice descriptive forms of political science or history and those who practice more mathematical forms. These conflicts sometimes paralyze the process of hiring new faculty, because the existing faculty cannot agree about the value of the new approach. This type of generational conflict usually cures itself over a period of years. If the new approach is a fad, as it often is, then it will not affect the composition of university departments for very long. On the other hand, if it really represents progress in the field, then its proponents are likely to become the dominant force at universities, as the proponents of the old practice gradually leave the scene and are replaced by those more comfortable with the new methods.

This problem is related to a general difficulty with elitism, which is the possibility that a group of leaders in some field becomes so convinced of the eternal significance of its own work that it acts to suppress, by whatever means are available to it, alternative approaches to the same subject. For example, the faculty of a department at one university may refuse to appoint new faculty members who take a different approach to their discipline than that of the existing members. This has happened many times, especially in fields where there are uncertain standards for merit, or deep disagreements about what is important in the field. It is too much to expect that fallible humans will evaluate themselves and their work so objectively that they would willingly abandon an institution they have been identified with to those they consider intellectual barbarians. However, it is a happy aspect of the organization of American society that any such control is relatively localized. Those who follow one approach to a discipline may control a department at one university or a group of universities, but there are enough other universities so that someone who is strongly motivated to follow an alternative approach can find a place to do so.

Such disagreements about the value of specific areas of a discipline may result in short-term departures from the principle of hiring and promoting people on the basis of merit but do not usually interfere with it for very long. A university faculty that holds out indefinitely against a valid new trend in some field is likely to find that it is no longer among the best departments in the field and hasten to correct its errors. A university that goes too far in filling its faculties with followers of some new intellectual fad will soon find that the students it produces are unable to make their way outside the university, and be forced to rethink its priorities.

Another, more serious, situation in which a conflict between competing schools of thought often arises occurs when the activity of the institution becomes subordinated, in the view of some of its members, to some "higher" aim, usually ideological or political in nature. This is a perennial problem in the social sciences. It is less common in the natural sciences, although some natural scientists have tried to impose their ideological views on the membership of other departments at their universities. When such ideological divisions occur, as apparently has happened recently at Harvard Law School, those on either side of the ideological divide may come to feel that it is more important to appoint members of their own faction than to find the most able candidates. Indeed, their evaluations may be determined by the views of these various candidates about whatever ideological dispute is at hand. For a long time no avowed Marxist was likely to be appointed to a professorship in economics or history at any American university. This situation was not entirely the result of government pressure, although that was a contributing factor. There was also some feeling among university social-science faculties that keeping Marxists out of universities was more important than finding the most able faculty members, or that being a Marxist was itself sufficient indication of academic incompetence.

While the exclusion of Marxists is no longer a general rule of procedure at American universities, it has in some instances been replaced by exclusions that are similarly motivated by ideology. For example, there has been systematic persecution, by ideologues inside and outside universities, of people such as educational psychologist Arthur Jensen and sociobiologist E. O. Wilson. The ideology of many of those who carry out this type of persecution is an extreme version of the view that all differences between individuals are due to upbringing or to motivation rather than to innate factors. The forms of persecution have ranged from verbal attacks to physical violence. The willingness of the ideologues to go beyond the bounds of decency in their crusade to keep universities from hearing views that contradict those that they approve has made it highly unlikely that someone who openly advocates the view that intelligence has a strong hereditary component would be appointed to the faculty of a leading American university, either in a field such as psychology, in which the view might be relevant to an appointment, or in fields in which it would be completely irrelevant. This situation is almost entirely unrelated to any intellectual merits that the position has or lacks. Rather, it is a consequence of the willingness of some ideologues to use indefensible methods against those whose views they oppose.

This attitude of the academic ideologues is the mirror image of the exclusionary policies of an earlier time, some of which were used against the very group of people who now want to enforce a new purity of thought. Their attempt to do this is as subversive to the achievement of quality among university faculties as anti-Marxist or anti-atheist policies once were.

Ideological considerations have come to play a role in university appointments in part because in many disciplines it is difficult to determine merit. When there are real disagreements about the central core of a subject, it becomes easy to substitute other criteria for the determination of merit. When even those who are most deeply concerned with a discipline cannot agree on what is most important, elitism becomes a very difficult attitude to apply to that discipline. Happily, there are a large number of academic disciplines for which such disagreement is minimal or absent, so that it is not difficult to determine intellectual merit.

Of course, there are circumstances other than ideological crusades in which elitist institutions have failed to use the criterion of high performance in selecting their membership. Race, religion, and gender are just some of the grounds that have inappropriately been used instead of merit to choose or to exclude members of these institutions. These practices were much more prevalent in the past, when even the best universities were not so explicitly dedicated to achieving the highest standards of scholarship. But such practices still exist in some cases, with somewhat different groups being excluded. Many universities in recent years have had bitter disputes about the hiring or firing of individuals who have not been evaluated on their merits because of biases among those making the decisions.

When such exclusions happen, the institutions that practice them compromise their basic aim, which is to achieve the highest level of performance of the intellectual activities for which they were created. To the extent that elitist institutions are currently still making such arbitrary exclusions, they should be condemned as not living up to their expressed aims. Those guilty of such practices should be stripped of the power to influence future decisions.

However, the conclusion that a specific institution or university in general is biased in choosing its faculty should be based on actual practices, not on an unjustified inference that such practices exist. The fact that the members of many elitist institutions of all types do not have the same distribution as the total population with regard to race, religion, or gender is not by itself evidence for exclusion of worthy candidates. There is no reason to expect that the talents required for each worthwhile activity are distributed in the same way among different groups. Indeed, there is a good deal of evidence to the contrary. For example, in the existing population of twenty-one-year-olds, an objective evaluation of talents will show that more men than women can solve difficult mathematics problems. Given that such differences occur in the population, elitist institutions would be less effective at carrying out their designated activities if their membership did not mirror these differences in the talents required to carry out these activities.

Affirmative-action programs began as an effort toward the elimination of actual bias in hiring or promotion. However, many of them have gone beyond this and have as their goal the achievement of a distribution of members within an elitist institution, such as a college faculty, that is the same as the distribution of targeted groups in the general population. These programs have not had much direct effect on the composition of college faculties, although they have forced faculty members to do immense amounts of paperwork in order to prove that they are actually doing what they say they are—trying to hire the most qualified people to teach and do research. What is the basis of affirmative-action programs that aim toward a specific population distribution for the membership of a faculty? Their justification relies either on the explicit—and, I believe, erroneous—assumption that the talents necessary for success in each field are randomly distributed in the population, or on the implicit assumption that the activity of the institution is not worth doing as well as possible. These assumptions are not made about such elitist athletic institutions as the Los Angeles Lakers basketball team, whose membership distribution among population subgroups is also not a mirror of the distribution in the population as a whole. Those academics who, in the name of social justice, are unwilling to accept the consequences of elitism with regard to the membership of their institutions but accept it unquestioningly at athletic institutions are really saying that the academic work done at universities is less worthwhile than what is done in football stadiums. They are surely entitled to that opinion, but it should not remain unchallenged by intellectual opposition from those of us who consider it absurd.

Recently there has been discussion at universities about a different type of "affirmative action," involving not persons but ideas. Many universities teach courses, such as Columbia's Contemporary Civilization or Humanities, that require all the students to read a specific set of books, selected from those that are considered to be of special merit or that have been extremely influential on the development of American society. This practice has been criticized by groups within the university who object to the fact that insufficient attention is paid to other works not included among those that everyone is required to read. For example, it has been argued that the literary works include too few by African, Asian, or female writers. Also, it has been argued that by emphasizing the development of European and American culture, the courses slight other cultures, making it appear to the students that these are less worthy.

Although there are some positive things to be said about this concept of affirmative action for ideas, I think that for the most part it is misguided. There are lessons to be learned from the study of other cultures, and college students should have the opportunity to do this. Also, many students who enter college have already read several of the standard works that are found in the typical Great Books course, and a case can be made that they will learn more from the study of other books than they would from a more sophisticated analysis of the same works.

However, courses of university study are necessarily limited in scope. In four years of study, a student will attend some 1,250 hours of lectures, not nearly enough time to cover the full content of human culture. Necessarily, choices must be made as to what topics or works are most worthwhile for study. There are two aspects of such choices. The specific works to be included in each course should be determined by those teaching the course, who are usually experts on that particular subject. This decision should be made solely on the grounds of the merit of the works. If the experts in a field do not believe that a work has high value according to the standards of merit prevailing in their discipline, it is a clear violation of the principles of elitist universities for others who are not experts to instruct them to believe otherwise.

The other choice concerns the decision about which topics should be included in the general requirements for education. This question is more complex, as it cuts across ordinary disciplinary lines, and must be made by the faculty as a whole. Universities vary a good deal in their general course requirements, and these requirements have changed considerably over the years, although not according to any regular pattern. A solution to this difficult problem is not the purpose of this article. Unlike such authors as Allan Bloom, I do not think that there is a unique answer that all universities should adopt to the question of how to balance the claims to a place in the curriculum among such subjects as natural science, social science, mathematics, and the humanities. However, it seems obvious that whatever the basis for such a decision, it should be made on academic grounds and should be immune to transient ideological pressures. Some universities, including my own, have considered changing their required courses of study because of actual or threatened demonstrations by groups of students who have objected to some aspects of the existing requirements. In my opinion, decisions made on this basis are an indication of academic incompetence, both on the part of the students demanding such changes and of the faculty who assent to them. It is as inappropriate for a faculty to change its curriculum in order to assuage student protesters as it would be inappropriate for the faculty to change the curriculum in order to mollify a legislature that finds the content of that curriculum subversive of public morals.

An issue related to those I have discussed is whether we should have "schools" devoted to the training of future members of elitist institutions. This procedure is widely followed in other countries, and to some extent is accepted in America. Institutions such as the Juilliard School for music, Stuyvesant High School for science, and the University of Oklahoma for football all play the role of preparing those who will eventually staff the various elitist institutions of America. However, this type of concentration of talented students in a few institutions has never gone as far here as in countries such as France, where, for example, almost all the future mathematicians attend one or two universities. Admission to such training schools is very important because, while innate ability is necessary, in most cases it is not sufficient to achieve the highest levels of performance without adequate training and motivation, both of which the schools can help furnish.

These training schools employ teachers or coaches who are more able than most to teach the skills needed in the activities that the students will someday perform. The curriculum to which the students are exposed is strongly focused on preparing them for these activities. Finally, students are exposed to others whose interests and abilities are similar to their own. As a product of one such school, the Bronx High School of Science, I can testify that the last of these features is in many ways the most important. The interaction with other bright students who were interested in science was one of the most important influences on my career and on those of many of my classmates.

The training schools' success in producing leaders in the various fields in which they operate has not spared them from criticism. As usual, this criticism has concentrated on schools that train intellectually able students, as opposed to those that train athletically or artistically able students. The main thrust of the criticism has been that by concentrating the able students at a few schools, we are shortchanging the students who remain at other schools. The injuries that are supposedly being done to those students not at the special schools include not getting the best teachers, not getting sufficient financial support, and being deprived of beneficial exposure to the more able students who have been removed to the special schools. Many of these criticisms have been applied specifically to schools supported by some government body, but some of the criticism has been applied to any school devoted to training able students, however it is supported.

I think this type of criticism is almost entirely misdirected. When it has been taken seriously and acted upon, there has been substantial harm both to society and to the able students who have been deprived of the opportunity to reach the highest levels allowed by their talents. Of these anti-elitist criticisms, the one that is most seriously wrong both on moral and on practical grounds is the one that calls for sacrificing the welfare of the more able students in order to obtain some benefits for the less able. There is no reason to expect that a student who is talented in mathematics, for example, would choose freely to remain in a class with those less able, in the hope that his presence there would somehow stir the others to higher achievement. This practice amounts to subordinating the educational interests of some individuals to those of others, and it strongly violates a basic principle of our social organization—that no person should be regarded by society as a means to some end of another person. As Kant wrote in the *Metaphysics of Morals*: "Every man is to be respected as an absolute end in himself; and it is a crime against the dignity that belongs to him as a human being, to use him as a means for some external purpose."

This argument against special schools is also doubtful on factual grounds. There is evidence that when numbers of able students are brought together in the same class or school, it has a beneficial "cluster effect" on the performance of each student. However, there is little indication that being taught together with more able students has a similar beneficial effect on those of little talent. Indeed, there is anecdotal evidence that being in a class with much brighter students can discourage others from learning.

It has sometimes been claimed that keeping talented students in the same schools and classes as the less talented is really for their own good. The argument is that this practice allows the talented students to see what the "real world" is like, whereas putting them in a school of their own would insulate them from contact with the majority population, with whom they will eventually have to interact. This argument suggests a complete lack of knowledge by those who make it of the situation of the talented in a typical school setting. To the extent that the talented have a problem in interacting with others, it is much more severe for children, for whom there is so much influence of peer pressure, than for adults, whose character is more fully formed. Able students have often complained about unpleasant experiences in situations in which they were the only people at a school interested in science or music or whatever their passion was, whereas it is rare to hear them complain about being at a school with other talented students.

The claim that establishing special schools for students of high ability deprives the less able students of good teachers is also of little merit. Anyone who has observed college teachers knows that teaching students with great talent in some field requires a different approach and different abilities from those needed to teach the subject to the average student, and there is little reason to doubt that this is true at other educational levels as well. Furthermore, as I have found in my own teaching career, groups of heterogeneous ability are intrinsically more difficult to teach than more homogeneous groups because of the problem in finding the right level at which to teach. In a group of students with widely varying ability, it is very difficult to avoid either boring the more able students or mystifying the less able ones. In many cases, teachers who are able to do one cannot do the other.

What of the argument that, by devoting financial resources to educating the talented, society is stinting on resources for the less talented? If this were valid it would indeed be a serious criticism, but it is probably not valid. Most of the recent thrust of educational concern in America has involved those who for various reasons fall below the average of educational achievement. Such concern is indeed warranted by the sorry state of much of the education that we give to underachievers. However, this neglect of weak students has diverted us from another concern—the education we give to the best of our students. Here, also, we fall far short of what we could do. Specialized training programs for students of high ability, such as the Columbia University program for secondary-school students with talent in science and mathematics, are available only to a small fraction of the students who could benefit from them.

The truth is that in most places, there are no programs at all for educating the highly talented, and where programs do exist, the resources devoted to them are a small fraction of those used to educate those with subnormal abilities, or those who have behavioral problems. The proportion of the overall educational resources used to train the highly able is so small that, far from using too much of our educational resources on them, we err in the opposite direction, by not providing those talented students with training that would allow them to make full use of their abilities. When we neglect the needs of our best students for an appropriate education, we shortchange these students and fail to develop intellectual resources that could be of great future benefit to society.

A problem that does exist for schools that train talented students is how to determine who should be given such training. The age at which great ability can be easily recognized varies from one discipline to another. For musical performance, it can be done quite early, before the age of ten. For mathematics, it can be done in the early teens, while for less symbolic sciences, such as biology, it probably cannot be done before college. It would be a good idea to have a national testing program for those abilities—athletic, intellectual, and artistic—that can be reliably detected at an early age. If such a program were set up, youngsters who did extremely well on the tests could be identified as candidates for training to help them succeed at the activities that would make use of their abilities. This would help eliminate situations in which talented students are deprived of training because their abilities are not recognized. It is quite possible that in our present haphazard system, we are not identifying many of the children who have such abilities. It is very important to identify such students early enough to enable them to make use of their abilities. But the tests that we have available are not infallible guides to later performance. Possibly better tests to predict high achievement could be devised if we set to work on it. In the meantime we should make sure that the route to eventual membership in elitist institutions is not closed to those who did not test well when young. To the greatest extent possible, we should monitor the work of those who are not in the specialized training schools, in order to find any talented students who have been missed by the selection process. It would, for example, be foolish to foreclose the opportunity for someone to become a mathematician just because he or she did badly on a test at age twelve.

There is one objection to elitist institutions that is not usually made explicit, but which is probably the underlying reason for much of the criticism of them. Our society is committed to achieving many things. One of our aims is a form of social equality. We want to avoid having legal or social distinctions between people that are based on accidents of birth. Another aim of society is that we wish to promote those activities that are generally recognized as worthy. Some tensions exist between the accomplishment of these aims. In striving to achieve excellent results in those activities that require exceptional abilities, we must distinguish those that possess such abilities. Those who are chosen in this way often obtain financial and social advantages over those not chosen. This problem of excessive rewards for talent is most severe for those whose activities are related to some type of entertainment, who can in many cases earn hundreds of times as much for their work as the average citizen. It is this type of result that is probably the ultimate objection to elitism. If there were no social or financial advantages ensuing from membership in elite institutions, then there would probably be few objections to them.

It may not be possible to avoid completely the correlation between high achievement and social rewards. But to give up the criterion of merit because it leads to social inequalities is to raise social equality above all the other principles of our society. This could easily result in a society in which we are all equally miserable. There are surely ways to avoid a situation in which those with talents are excessively rewarded, without discouraging them from using their talent at all. For example, it is not the social and financial rewards given to faculty members of elite universities that are their prime motivation toward high achievement. The most able of the faculty whom I know are mainly internally motivated, by the desire to do as well as they can in their chosen field of work. I expect that the same is true for members of many other elite institutions, such as symphony orchestras. Convincing people that a high level of achievement is its own best reward is probably the most effective way of diminishing the social inequalities of elitism.

Perhaps if it were considered desirable, we could work toward the goal of a society in which each person could accomplish anything that anyone else can do. Alternatively, we might be able to arrange that everyone be talented in at least one of the activities that society considers worthwhile. Achieving either type of society would probably require a substantial amount of interference in personal freedom, in such matters as the raising of children. In any case, neither of these possibilities has been realized anywhere in our present world. Given that talents are not the same for everybody, and that we have limited capacity to train those without native ability to achieve high levels of performance, society must choose between two alternatives. One is to encourage strongly those who can do extremely well at the things that we consider worthwhile, accepting that this will lead to some greater financial and social rewards to those with talent for those worthwhile activities. The other is to accept a substantially lesser degree of achievement of these activities, in the name of minimizing distinctions in how different individuals fare in life. Whenever people have been given a choice between these alternative strategies, they have chosen to identify and to reward the talented, while correctly insisting that no artificial barriers should exist to determining those with real talent. There is no popular enthusiasm for anti-elitism in fields in which high achievement is possible. The weakness of the case made by the proponents of anti-elitism cannot be strengthened by appealing to the will of the people. Those of us who value high achievement wherever it is found should not allow the arguments of the anti-elitists to be used to undermine the work of the institutions whose membership they criticize. It is folly to try to further one set of worthy ends by making it impossible to carry out another equally worthy set. Elitist institutions have been responsible for some of the best achievements of our society, and it would be tragic to prevent the future extension of these achievements by destroying these institutions.

Another Reality Club

JOAN RICHARDSON

The purpose of the Arensberg circle was to change the way human beings saw themselves in the world. This was really only the age-old function of the prophet. The members of the group saw their errand into the wilderness clearly: It was to create contexts, worlds within worlds, in their works of art, in which and through which those who were willing to submit themselves to the process illustrated and demanded by these works could perceive what it meant to live on the edge of experience in an ever-transforming present.

In New York between 1914 and 1921 there was another Reality Club. While it did not bear this or any other formal name, the principle on which it was organized was the same as ours—to bring together some of the best minds of the time and create an atmosphere in which their ideas would be both stimulated and shared. Walter Arensberg, a wealthy patron of the arts who brought the group together, was himself an intellectual heir to Francis Bacon, whose *New Atlantis* first suggested to Arensberg the pattern for his "reality club."

In his *New Atlantis* Bacon conjured a Utopia where luminaries of various disciplines lived and worked together in perfect harmony. This was a fiction. In reality the best way to approach this idea, Arensberg thought, was to provide the conditions that would at least prompt imperfect harmonies on a regular basis. And so for seven years Arensberg and his wife, Louise, opened their studio apartment on West Sixty-seventh Street off Central Park West to the stars of New York's new-world universe. These included, at different times, Marcel Duchamp, Francis Picabia, Albert Gleizes, William Carlos Williams, Man Ray, Mina Loy, Edgard Varèse, Walter Pach, Walt Kuhn, Arthur Davies, Carl Van Vechten, and Beatrice Wood.

As is apparent from this list of names, there was one major difference between Arensberg's "reality club" and ours—the presence and participation of scientists and mathematicians. So while the earlier group shared with us a common pursuit, the nature of the talks and activities was quite different. It must not be supposed, however, that the participants were scientifically illiterate. Quite the contrary; Arensberg, acting always as the informal director of gatherings, made certain that his "New Atlantans" kept themselves current with each development that revealed something more about reality. And there was a great deal to keep up with during these years as the Great War raging across the Atlantic threatened to destroy the faith in science that had produced, together with wondrous knowledge about things

99

seen and unseeable, the technology that was itself destroying more than eight million lives. Among the contributions and discoveries of the period were the following: Niels Bohr's formulation of atomic structure; Robert Goddard's rocketry experiments; Albert Einstein's general theory of relativity; Sir Arthur Eddington's investigations of the physical properties of stars; Max Planck's introduction of quantum theory; Harlow Shapley's determination of the dimensions of the Milky Way and Max Wolf's mapping of its true structure; Vilhjalmur Stefansson's exploration north of the Arctic Circle; Ernest Shackleton's expedition to the Antarctic; and Ernest Rutherford's uncovering of a subatomic universe. Whether in the form of readings about these events and researches prepared and assigned to the group for future discussion or from information provided by an invited speaker, Arensberg provided real food for the thoughts of the various poets, painters, musicians, and others who met regularly in his comfortable home.

At each meeting copious quantities of exquisitely prepared foods and delicacies were well balanced by constantly flowing beverages. There were games, music, readings, whispered discussions in corners, and more than occasional bizarre behavior on the parts of one, two, three, four, or more of the geniuses who happened to be present on a given evening. The Baroness Elsa von Freytag-Loringhoven, for example, who seems to have been particularly drawn to the poets in the group, was always ready to shed all her clothes and parade herself as the most successful example of a "ready-made." And then there was Mina Loy, herself a poet, who one evening together with Marcel Duchamp, Beatrice Wood, Arlene Dresser, and Charles Demuth excused herself from the larger company to enjoy group sex in Duchamp's bed, conveniently located in the adjoining studio Arensberg had generously provided for the expatriate French artist.

The games were not all this exciting, however. Most, though playful, were serious. Again following the kind of thinking implicit in Francis Bacon's program for the *New Atlantis*, Arensberg set up activities that would stretch and tone the minds of his friends. There was almost always a chess game between Arensberg and Duchamp; others could look on or play their own game on another board. The poets of the group were asked to construct poems around subtle puns and covert complex structures. On the reading of a new work, the "game" for the group was to discover the carefully hidden key. Similarly, Arensberg delighted in adding to his impressive avant-garde art collection—he had been actively involved in the presentation of the 1913 Armory Show, and many of the pieces that once hung at the show later found a home in his studio—paintings or other objects that taunted viewers with apparent nonsense. There were many pieces by Duchamp, both completed and in progress. His famous *Large Glass*, or *The Bride Stripped Bare by Her Bachelors, Even*, was worked on and completed while Duchamp lived on West Sixty-seventh Street. One of his ready-mades, his *Trébuchet* (from the French verb *trébucher*, meaning "to trip, stumble"), a coat rack with four metal hangers, was nailed to the floor of his studio. Henri Rousseau's *Merry Jesters* was another particularly intriguing puzzler. Arensberg himself was known to have stood for up to four hours before a canvas studying its meaning. He no doubt wanted his circle to enjoy a similar experience. The *Merry Jesters* depicts a family of what most closely resemble baboons, all staring out of the middle ground at an imagined audience. A baby bottle hangs in the place where one would expect a breast on the female baboon; the bottle squirts milk. A young baboon also looks out of the canvas, but from behind the mature animals. Two other mature animals play with what seem to be a back scratcher and a gardening tool. A cockatiel perches on a branch above, to the right of center; a sprig of foxglove symbolically balances the bird on the left side of the canvas. These are the only interruptions to the dense green jungle foliage characteristic of Rousseau's paintings and meticulously rendered here. Members of the group spent hours trying to unlock the conundrum presented by this fanciful work.

Together with this and the Duchamps, Cézanne, Braque, Brancusi, Picasso, Matisse, Picabia, Sheeler, Derain, Joseph Stella, and Renoir were also well represented in Arensberg's collection. In addition, there were many African and pre-Columbian pieces and occasional single items from other painters such as Giorgio di Chirico. Already in the second decade of the century, Arensberg was leading the avant-garde of the avant-garde. He was known in New York as the father of what would come to be called Dada, even before the movement was given its name at the Café Voltaire in Zurich in 1916.

But Arensberg and his friends had a much more serious intention than that usually attributed to the Dadaists, of shocking the bourgeoisie. While they did indeed scorn middle-class values and wholeheartedly rejected the Protestant work ethic that informed them, their purpose went beyond the specifically social aspect. The individuals who gathered regularly in the West Sixty-seventh Street apartment were acutely aware that reality as they had been educated to know it no longer existed. The impact of Darwin's discovery of our common ancestor as "a hairy quadruped, mostly arboreal in its habits," had been felt. Nietzsche had proclaimed the death of God, Freud had uncovered the unknown within each breast, and Einstein had described an unimaginable universe. In this climate, even "the absence of imagination itself had to be imagined," as Wallace Stevens, another of the members of the Arensberg circle, put it. The poetry, music, painting, and sculpture of those who attempted to grapple with the idea of the new world they inhabited was characterized by features alien to what had come to be accepted as art until this burdened moment.

The most general and striking of these features was the apparent irreverence for the past displayed in the break from the traditional forms of representing reality. The most subtle feature was a pervasive undertone of irony that colored even what seemed to be the most purely aesthetic, abstract renderings. The most obvious of these stylistic shifts was the breaking up of pictorial surface into several planes that characterized cubism. The strongest effect of this device was to destroy the distinction between background and foreground, decentering the "subject" from the privileged position it had enjoyed in perspectival depictions. From one side this mimicked the change in the way human beings saw themselves in relationship to the historical and natural orders and to their personal, unconscious order, hidden from yet motivating them. In this sense, the decentering symbolized the actual feeling of dislocation experienced by those who allowed themselves to remain open to what the discoveries of Darwin and Freud meant. The individual could no longer be understood as something separate from the background that had produced him or her. Cubism and the other new forms reflected this breakup of an integrated identity.

Seen from another side, this reflected the aesthetic translation of Kant's perception of the indivisibility of inner and outer realms: that the understanding of reality must come not from placing inner against outer but from understanding the fused and interdependent relation between them. Since the bases of this relation are time and space, the relation constantly changes, shifts in the way cubist presentations tried to imitate. It is impossible to see all the aspects of the "subject" of a cubist canvas at once, in the same way it is impossible to see both chalice and two facing profiles in the illustration so often used to make this point about perception—the point taken as the meaning of a "relativistic" view of the pictorial plane.

In terms of cubist aesthetic and method, this was articulated in two fundamental ways, one having to do with time, the other with space. The primary apprehension concerning time was that no subject or object could be experienced fully if the subject or object was separated from past knowledge of it. The representation of reality was "truer" when the thing known was presented incorporating some record of previous experience. The various intersecting and juxtaposed spatial forms of a cubist canvas were intended to mirror this constant movement of consciousness, aware of itself as it observed something external that temporarily focused attention.

Extending this understanding to its extreme, Marcel Duchamp eventually abandoned even the canvas that created a barrier between observer and ground beyond the work. The *Large Glass* includes the ever-shifting present background seen through the glass but incorporated by its frame.

As early as the eighteenth century, there had been experimentation in representing a new understanding of time—in Mozart's restructuring of phrasing, for example. But not until the early twentieth century, as art became as self-conscious as consciousness itself had become with Kant and Hegel, were these aesthetic developments formalized. The philosopher who first handled these effects in a direct and practical way, examining them from various angles as if he himself were a cubist painter, was Henri Bergson, who, appropriately, wrote seminal pieces on consciousness, time, and laughter. This work was translated and published serially in Alfred Stieglitz's *Camera Work*. *Camera Work* (in which Gertrude Stein's work was first published in America as well), together with Freud's *Interpretation of Dreams* and certain other key texts, constituted required reading for the members of the Arensberg circle.

In translating the new understanding of time into formal artistic elements, painters, writers, and musicians focused primarily on intervals and how varying intervals could be used to approximate the distinctions between the different kinds of time that were now being discussed. The music of Erik Satie, Igor Stravinsky, Darius Milhaud, and Arthur Honegger—played by Louise Arensberg and Edgard Varèse on the piano—illustrated this clearly for the group. In poetry, too, there was an attempt to create other kinds of time intervals. By using titles that were puzzling, for example, poets hoped, in part, to force pauses or rests, spaces where the listeners or readers could try to figure out the relationship between title and poem. Asian masters had earlier established the same kind of tension in their koans. This aspect was linked to a comic element. For Zen masters the illogicality of a koan is intended to produce the laughter accompanying the realization of reason's limits; this experience is a moment of enlightenment when, according to one of their standard texts, the individual has the experience known as the "snow man," of melting into a sweat at the moment of illumination—a moment when the ego dissolves.

All these innovations, including the stress on the comic element, had behind them a serious philosophical intent. In the most general terms, the aim was to dissolve the distinction between subject and object, to solve the problem Descartes had set three centuries earlier; the attempt continues today.

In his *Masters of Modern Art*, Walter Pach, another of the regular members of the circle, gave a coherent account of the historical evolution of the new forms and named the different features of these forms, all of which play around the underlying theme of the identification of inner and outer, time and space, what is and what seems. In discussing the genesis of the modernist movement, he compared the early twentieth century to the Renaissance, noting how contemporary painters went to museums to broaden their bases of reference in the same way that the fifteenth-century painters looked to the classical past. This represented an intuitive attempt to obviate the limitations derived from the eighteenth century's mannered extension of one side of the Cartesian duality, which had, then, to be compensated for by the antithetical romantic excesses of the nineteenth. The extreme separation of the thinking subject, reason's instrument, from its organic sources prompted the romantic reaction, which, when it was later empirically evidenced and argued for by Darwin, in turn prompted the disguising reaction described by the term "Victorian." Imitating the Renaissance model represented, in large part, a desire to return to a point before the disjunction between humanity and nature, mind and body was made, in the hope that a synthesis could be achieved. By the end of the nineteenth century this attempt had produced the symbolist aesthetic. Symbolism stressed what Charles Baudelaire popularized as a system of "correspondences," linking the individual to nature and the universe in a way that echoed the fifteenth- and sixteenth-century neo-Platonists' interest in the Cabala and Hermeticism, both of which offered, in different forms, magical or mystical keys to unlock the secrets of the universe and the individual's connection with it.

Arensberg, Duchamp, and the rest of the circle were involved with the lore of the hermetic tradition. For Arensberg this interest had begun when he first became curious about Francis Bacon. In studying the literature of magic and alchemy, he learned the symbolism passed down through the centuries to characterize the processes that were necessary to the "Great Work" of finding the philosopher's stone and transmuting lead into gold. Becoming familiar with these terms helped him in his later work on the cryptography of Shakespeare (whom he, like many others around the turn of the century, believed to be identical with Francis Bacon) and Dante. He also made this arcane vocabulary available to the members of his circle so that they could make the games of their poems and paintings more challenging. Duchamp used alchemical symbols and references freely in his *Large Glass* while pointing directly to the "Great Work" with his title

(since, in French, *grand* means both "large" and "great"). Mina Loy
and Wallace Stevens, too, worked the method and iconography of the
hermetic tradition into their poetry.

The original purpose of the alchemists' "Great Work" was to
discover the philosopher's stone, the catalyst that would transform
base metals, like lead, into gold. By the fifteenth century, after
Paracelsus, this pursuit had already become a metaphor for finding the
gold understood as a medicinal unguent that would cure human ills.
By the time the idea itself became transmuted over the centuries,
separating the early alchemists from twentieth-century initiates, the
literal aspect had crystallized and been changed into chemistry, while
the metaphorical aspect had sublimed into the search for a spiritual
catalyst that would change the base elements of human experience
into a golden rule to help individuals live in a better way.

The purpose of the Arensberg circle was to change the way human
beings saw themselves in the world. This was really only the age-old
function of the prophet. The members of the group saw their errand
into the wilderness clearly: It was to create contexts, worlds within
worlds, in their works of art, in which and through which those who
were willing to submit themselves to the process illustrated and
demanded by these works could perceive what it meant to live on the
edge of experience in an ever-transforming present. This meant living
without the encumbrance of certainty provided by the various versions
of the Western myth of progress, which for nearly two millennia had
kept human beings' minds separated from their bodies. The myth had
succeeded so well that the mind's technology was in the process of
sacrificing the bodies of eight million young men at its altar.

The intention of those who met in Arensberg's studio was to restore
to human beings what Stevens once called the "instinct of joy."
Indulging this sense did not mean taking an easy step into laughing
at the surface details of experience or even at the deeper, ironic
condition of human life. What these individuals perceived was that
the closer one could approach pure *being*, without the interference of
distracting appearances—"Let be be finale of seem"—the closer one
came to joy, the pleasure of merely circulating. The more often and
the longer this state could be sustained, as Walter Pater had suggested

in his conclusion to *The Renaissance*, the more likely it became that one could understand something about the nature of nature—by regarding it not only from outside as an object of contemplation but knowing it from inside, as one with it, experiencing the self as matter being continuously transformed into spirit, feeling the waves of energy that are the universe move in and out, pass through the temporary container of the body. The individuals of the Arensberg group were working to provide, through their carefully constructed works, an access to perceiving reality at this level.

The stress that Duchamp, for example, laid on eros is at the center of this understanding, which is not surprising, since it is usually through eros that human beings first come into mature contact with their oneness with the universe. Duchamp was not alone in having this perception. Plato and the old Chinese sages knew it, and, among Duchamp's contemporaries, D. H. Lawrence, Sigmund Freud, and Havelock Ellis began from this premise. T. S. Eliot, too, began from it, seeing the Victorians' extreme divorce of mind from body as the cause of his personal predicament and the largest single factor contributing to the conditions that gave birth to World War I.

When Marcel Duchamp—alias Rrose Sélavy (a homonymic pun for *Eros c'est la vie* ["Eros is life"])—arrived in New York and began presenting his work, it seemed that he had experientially understood what Freud had started to lay out abstractly and clinically in his *Three Essays on the Theory of Sexuality*, subjects he would make both broader and more specific in *Civilization and Its Discontents*. Duchamp seemed to be illustrating, with two- and three-dimensional examples, precisely the problems and consequences Freud delineated.

One of the strongest points to come through Duchamp's work is a comment on the attitude toward sex of the Western, civilized individual around the period of the First World War. This showed itself in the content of his most important works of these years. In the *Large Glass*, what is depicted is a sexual act: the beginning causes of desire described in wholly mechanical terms that are, at the same time, allegorical forms for alchemical processes. When the *Large Glass* is considered together with his other work, the related *Nude Descending a Staircase* and *King and Queen Surrounded by Swift Nudes*, as well as with the production of his later years, it is plain that Duchamp was translating into the symbolic forms he presented his observation that the only way human beings of his generation seemed able to accept and deal with their sexual appetites was in dissociated, mechanical terms. This protected them from having to look closely at and admit, with the full range of feeling entailed, their animality. It was not uncontrolled ribaldry alone, then, that led Mina Loy and her playmates to Duchamp's bed. There was a method to this apparent madness. A new world, another reality, was being explored.

After seven years, the Arensbergs, actually quite conservative in their private manners, seem to have wearied of the expense and excitement of hosting their talented and eccentric company; they moved themselves and their by then well-noted art collection to California. (It is now part of the permanent collection of the Philadelphia Museum of Art.) The discoveries of the individuals who had been part of the circle continued, however. Almost every member of the Arensberg group went on to produce significant work or to contribute to creating contexts that made such work possible; a quick review of the names of the members attests to this. But the group did not sustain itself. Once its prime mover and presiding genius left New York, there were no more meetings, though occasionally two or three of the old circle met for lunch or dinner and shared news about their latest interests and work.

It is, I think, highly unusual and significant that almost all the members of the Arensberg circle made contributions that have in some way changed or influenced the way we experience the world around us. It was not that those who formed the group had already established their reputations—quite the opposite. What was it, then, that accounts for such a high success rate? Was it simply Arensberg's acuity in recognizing the signs of genius among those with whom he came in contact that led him to invite the chosen to his soirées? Or did the atmosphere Arensberg created trigger the response to what presented itself during the early years of the century as chaotic uncertainty?

Perhaps we today have grown too comfortable with uncertainty. We no longer seem to try to come up with individual solutions to the personal, social, historical, ethical, or aesthetic problems it presents. We accept, rather, certain words about uncertainty and go about our business. In part, those of us who are not fluent in the current scientific languages feel dependent on those who can explain some of what we don't understand. Unlike Arensberg and his company, who were admittedly and actively perplexed about the crisis in belief and knowledge generated by the contributions of Darwin, Freud, and Einstein, we seem to take the facts of these contributions in stride. We assume that the scientists will provide answers—and so we do not propose the right kinds of questions to ourselves or to others. I believe it is this situation that the present Reality Club addresses. The purpose of our gatherings is not to look simply *at* facts, but *through* them. Together we attempt to forge a common language with which questions can be posed and problems considered. With the understanding that this language can provide, we can each then go on to pursue our individual interests and to make our contributions.

Failure Is Nice—
Failure on a Computer
Is Even Better

ROGER SCHANK

Critics comment about what kind of child will come out of the computer age. They are concerned that children will be able to relate only to computers. I am concerned that children be educated at all, that they be excited by learning, that they not view their entire school career as preparation for the SATs. I am concerned that they stop being rewarded for the answers and start being rewarded for good questions.

Why is the use of computers in education so poorly understood? Everyone has an opinion on the subject, but few really seem to comprehend what all the fuss is about. Everyone believes that children must learn about computers. Everyone believes that computers will cause a revolution in education, or that they won't. Everyone has an opinion, but how many understand the issues? Very few, I am afraid. Very few indeed.

And why is the state of awareness about computers and their potential in education so poorly understood? This situation is actually quite easy to explain. When something is invented, people evaluate the invention on the basis of its usefulness at the time. Even the most enlightened of observers have difficulty basing an evaluation on what may happen in the distant future. Making such an evaluation is even more difficult if the right form of the invention is unavailable to evaluate. Who could imagine the effects of the gasoline engine when it hadn't yet been installed in its first automobile, yet alone its first airplane? Jet travel has completely changed the way we do business, take vacations, educate ourselves, conduct scientific matters, and handle political and military matters; yet, who could have guessed all the changes that would come from the invention of an engine only marginally related to those changes? Evaluating the potential uses of computers in education is like trying to understand the future of warfare by observing the use of airplanes in World War I. The world is changing so fast that discussions about today's computers are already discussions of the past.

Two points seem clear when the public evaluates the use of computers in the schools. First, almost all parents of school-age children favor having lots of computers in their children's schools. Computers are the mark of an advanced school system. Go to a town and ask about the quality of the school system. Someone will immediately cite the computers the school has just purchased as an example of how progressive or rich or modern the school is. Ask what the kids do with these machines, and a second fact becomes obvious: Parents don't know what the computers are used for. They do, of course, feel uneasy about the possibility that children may be learning less mathematics as a result. After all, the computers they are familiar with are calculators, and the more you use your calculator, the less you use your head. Gone are such important math skills as addition, because computers calculate better.

In any case, performing basic math skills seems to be what adults believe children do with computers. But what actually is the case? Every day in the schools that consider themselves quite enlightened and have purchased some computers to prove it, children troop down for their time in the computer room. Why do they go there? The reasons are complex.

Reason 1: They Go Because the Computer Room Is There. In today's competitive world, schools are rushing to beat each other to the punch. They are interested in proving to parents, school boards, legislatures, and alumni that they are right on top of the new trends, that they have bought the latest computer, and that the students are using it. Consequently, students had better use the thing.

As for the children, they are usually quite excited by the idea of using a computer. Computers are used to sell watches, cars, movies, televisions, and so on. Computers are good things. Once upon a time, only complete nerds knew or cared about computers. Thick glasses and lab coats were definitely *de rigueur* in the computer set or, at least, in the popular imagination of what the computer set looked like.

These days, all that has changed. The smartest kid in the class is expected to know about computers. Children of computer scientists are absolutely expected to know about computers. When I say that I'd rather see my children playing ball after school than staring at a CRT, I get perplexed looks. Computers are in. Knowing about computers is in. Children want to own a computer. Parents feel upset if they can't afford a computer for their children. Schools won't admit to not having one, and everyone agrees that the children should be thrilled to hurry over to the computer room when called upon to do so. And, actually, the children do want to go to the computer room. Why they want to go, apart from the reasons I have just mentioned, tells us a great deal about education today and, with some luck, about tomorrow.

Reason 2: They Go to Become Computer Literate. The teachers, parents, and principals of the current crop of schoolchildren consider themselves computer illiterate. When people such as my colleagues and I were tinkering with the monstrously slow and awkward computers of the fifties and sixties in our school labs, our peers, the vast majority of whom are now parents of schoolchildren, were carefully avoiding such machines and even the people who played with them. Today, they suddenly believe that they made a horrible error. Of course, for the most part, these people are no more interested in computers than they ever were, but they believe that their children, at least, should know all about them. And why should their children know about them? Because we live in the computer age. Because not knowing about computers will make one illiterate in the nineties and beyond. But, most of all, because parents are frightened that somehow the world is passing their children by.

Are they right? To what extent does one need to be computer literate? Actually, that term has always eluded me, but this year I was horrified to learn that my daughter was required to take a computer literacy course to graduate from the fancy private high school she attends. In the course, she learned about the history of computers, including the love affairs of their early inventors. She learned about bits and bytes, and she learned the names of all the pieces of the computer's hardware and some points about its software.

Worth knowing? Well, everything is worth knowing, after all. But why should the course be a graduation requirement? The answer, I suppose, is that people who don't know something about computers feel stupid. When the subject of computer literacy comes up, I always wonder why people don't feel equally stupid about not knowing how to fix their cars when they break down or how to get the well to work when there is no water in the house—neither subject being a graduation requirement at my daughter's school. As for me, I would imagine these two literacies to be more important for almost everyone, including me, if being literate means knowing about how the sorting machines of the 1800s relate to the computers we use today.

Obviously, what computer literacy really means is that someone needs to figure out why those expensive machines were purchased in the first place. When it comes to the question, What knowledge of a given machine must we acquire, the answer usually is, knowing how to use it in ways that would be genuinely helpful in our lives. This answer holds no less true for computers. But teaching children how to use computers in this way requires proficient teachers, and any teachers who are that good at teaching computers presumably are also good at using computers, a skill that would immediately entitle them to three or four times their salaries as teachers.

So, what is computer literacy? It's a double-edged sword. One edge is labeled, "We spent all this money for something, didn't we?" and the other, "The teachers and administration don't know what these things are for, but we are sure the students will figure it out if we make them use them."

Reason 3: They Go to Play Computer Games. And what do the little tykes do when they get down to the computer room? What is all the fuss about? When a child rushes home to tell Mommy, "I used a computer today!" and Mommy is so thrilled, what did the child actually do? For the most part, the young computer student ran a few programs or, perhaps, used a word processor. Well, word processors can be very interesting. They are today's typewriters. But how excited would Mommy be to hear, "Today I learned a modern typing technique"? No thrill there. And the programs? What does it mean for children to run programs? Maybe they press some keys, and some pretty pictures appear. Or maybe they play Space Invaders or Zork. That's what gets kids excited about computers. They are trucked down to the computer room to be at a video arcade—and on school time even.

Do children like to go to the computer room because they can play games on school time? Actually, a very large part of their willingness to go does derive from their interest in playing games. But children not only like to play games, they like to be on their own, out of the controlled environment of the classroom. No wonder they value their time on the computer.

A lesson can be learned here, though. Suppose that what the children were doing on the computer were educationally relevant. Couldn't games important for children to play be constructed? Or, to put this another way, couldn't educational material be presented like a game that a child could control in the one-on-one environment of the computer? Of course, such material could be and, to a limited extent, has been developed for the computer.

Why isn't more of it available? Because developing computer software simply costs a great deal of money. Most of the software that has been marketed for children has been developed to sell to children, and that means noise and rockets before real educational value. The schools that want software with educational value also need to band together to demand what they want. Sadly, that hasn't happened enough to make the development of high-quality educational software economically worthwhile for a software developer. Besides, no general agreement stands on what to develop. No one knows what good educational software should look like.

For the foreseeable future, games will rule the computer roost; children will be happy to go to the computer room; teachers will be happy to send them there; and parents will be happy to pay for it. Everyone will be happy, but no one will learn much.

Reason 4: They Go to Learn Something Worth Learning. Children do go to the computer room to learn something worth learning. Children want to learn. The question is whether the school system wants to teach. In general, one can't learn that many things on a computer. I don't mean that one can't, in principle, learn anything. I mean that one cannot learn without the software to teach the material. Moreover, one can't learn what the teachers don't know how to teach. We can see a wonderful example of the absurdity of the computer world and children by looking at LOGO.

So many people have misunderstood LOGO and the work of Seymour Papert that the record should be put straight. But, before I do that, let me say a word about learning to program. Should children learn to program? Why not? It's a useful mental exercise, sort of like learning mathematics or Latin—but perhaps that demeans it. Learning to program means learning to produce step-by-step procedures that characterize processes. You really can learn to understand the processes behind what you are programming when you are forced to take the time to do a step-by-step analysis of it.

Learning to program has two parts: the step-by-step analysis and the translation of that analysis into a language the computer can understand, such as BASIC or FORTRAN. The first part is where the thinking is. You barely need a computer for this. Rather, you need more or less just the idea of a computer. What is taught when schoolchildren are taught to program? The second part, naturally. Children are taught boring, arbitrary, obnoxious programming languages. The teachers aren't really at fault; they don't know what else to teach. Nevertheless, for the most part, programming is taught wrongly in the schools—which brings me back to Papert.

One of the ways to teach programming in the schools is by having children learn LOGO, a computer game invented by Seymour Papert of M.I.T. for the purpose of teaching children mathematics. One problem with how mathematics is taught is the emphasis on finding the right answers. Papert addressed that problem in LOGO by making discovery the emphasis. His idea was to get children to explore mathematical concepts by exploring the consequences of their actions. LOGO gave children a simple language in which to instruct the computer about what they wanted to explore in mathematics.

LOGO is a great idea, a great game for children to play, and I by no means intend to denigrate the idea by calling it a game. Learning should be fun, and exploring new territory almost always is. LOGO is the language one learns for exploring the territory. That was the idea, anyway. Unfortunately, the idea and the use of the idea don't have a lot in common. The problem is that LOGO is, of course, a programming language. Moreover, it is a simple programming language, one that was designed for children to learn easily. So, if you want your children to learn to program—because that's what computers are for, aren't they?—then teach them LOGO. Presto, your children know how to program a computer—but, so what?

The "so what" is clear enough. Now children know how to use computers, they can program—and their are parents impressed. But what exactly is the value of knowing how to program? This question has three possible answers, each of which has little to do with why parents want their kids to program. The first is that learning to program enables you to find work as a programmer. Schools, however, really aren't set up to provide this kind of professional training, nor should they be, and gaining professional training is probably not what excites parents about their kids' learning to program, anyway.

The second answer is that learning to program has no value. Since they assume that their children will need this skill (otherwise, why would a school have computers?) parents usually counter with, "But what if they need to write a program some day?" The reality is that children who have learned to program often can do very little with this knowledge. What programs should they write? They don't really need to write any. Increasingly, we are nearing the day when all the programs that students might need already have been written. Of course, learning to program has value if programming is a skill one needs in one's professional life. Scientists need to write new programs as new problems come up. For most people, though, programming isn't a need that is going to come up too often.

Actually, I do believe that learning to program is a worthwhile pursuit, and this is the third answer. Programming enhances thinking skills. Computers are so stupid that if you don't tell them what to do in every detail, they won't do what you ask. Learning to talk to a computer in this tedious way is a valuable exercise in precise thinking. Computers, therefore, should be taught as part of a curriculum in thinking.

Tell this to parents, however, and out go the computers. Parents want up-to-date schools and up-to-date kids. Parents are impressed that their kids can program because they themselves cannot. And, until most parents can program, this nonsense is likely to continue.

Nevertheless, since LOGO is what children are learning in schools, let's return to it. LOGO was designed to teach thinking first and mathematics second. The genius behind it, as with most ingenious ideas, was both a matter of timing and a matter of reorientation. Let me address the latter first. Too often, when we are taught a subject in school, we are taught the facts—"Just the facts, ma'am," as Sergeant Friday used to say. Mathematics education has always had exactly this flavor, and it still does, I am sorry to say. Papert's idea was that, with the advent of computers, one could change the game a bit. Given a child and an idea and a computer, one can get the child to test the idea on the computer. That, in a nutshell, is the concept behind LOGO. Let the child construct a hypothesis and construct a procedure for testing that hypothesis. Testing hypotheses is what LOGO is all about. LOGO itself is another one of those boring computer languages, but when learned, it allows a child to test his ideas. The power of that possibility should not be underestimated. Papert was, and is, trying to let children think. If computers could do that—now, *that* would be something.

This discussion brings me to the first point, which is that of timing. Papert's idea was particularly nice because it preceded by a great many years the advent of the so-called personal computer. Thus, when schools became able to buy cheap computing power for their students, LOGO was there. It had been tested, optimized, expanded, and made easier, and it was ready to sell on any piece of equipment. I have a feeling that, unfortunately, Papert never made much money on LOGO; if the world were a just place, he would have.

The history of LOGO brings me to the problem of the current state of educational software. Papert was first, but he was also alone. So, when personal computers became available, and software was needed for them, especially because children were the target of the computer manufacturers' sales pitch, educational software began to be produced in abundance. And did the producers of that software follow Papert's model? Did they seek to replicate the success that had gone before? No. A thousand times no.

Why not? The answer is quite simple: In general, two classes of people were interested in building such software. The first class consisted of the computer types who recognized the demand for educational software, who knew how to build computer games, and who figured that they knew enough about education to design software. So they built games in which children could shoot down the verb as it flew by and other such educational masterpieces.

Their products were better, for the most part, than those of the second class—educators who, knowing nothing about computers, built programs that strongly resembled books. The child was asked to read a page; to press *a, b, c,* or *d* as an answer to a question about the passage; and then to press the return key for the next page.

As time goes on, an increasing number of educators and others claim that computers have no place in the schools. It might seem, from what I have said so far, that I am one of them. Actually, most of the people who are against computers in the schools are against them because of the software that already exists. They have seen the reality, and they don't like it. I don't blame them. In fact, if you look at the preponderance of junk on the market, you will conclude that computers have no place in education.

But the market has responded as markets tend to do. No one has bought much of that stuff, and the companies that have produced it or sold it are more or less out of business. But what about computers and education? Can computers successfully be employed as a means of educating children? Should we throw away all the computers and wait to see what happens?

We need to design computer software that makes sense from an educational point of view. The issue is not what is available, but what could be available. The issue is not what LOGO is or is not, but how children can become creative by using a computer to formulate and to test hypotheses about things they have never thought about before. That is the power of computers. That is the hope of people like Papert, and it is my hope as well.

Widespread disagreement has arisen over the value of LOGO as well, of course. Because Papert wanted so much to influence teachers of mathematics, he has adopted the strategy of talking about the teaching of reasoning. When one teaches reasoning, however, one is tempted to talk about general reasoning skills. Sometimes good things are sold on bad premises; then, the good things don't get bought. The good thing here is LOGO; the bad premise, that it teaches general reasoning skills.

In artificial intelligence (AI) research, with respect to problem solving, early attempts revolved around creating programs with general reasoning skills. These days, many researchers have realized that general reasoning may not exist and that teaching specific skills to computers, making them miniexperts in fairly confined arenas, rather than general repositories of wisdom, may be easier. The reasons for this are clear enough. When we go to a doctor because we are sick, we do not go to the smartest person in town in the hope that he can figure out our problem. We go to someone trained in medicine, who we hope has seen our malady before and knows exactly what to do about it. We don't much care whether our doctors have general reasoning skills. We want them to have the facts and lots of specific reasoning skills— the more specific to our particular problem, the better.

Of course, this wish on our part doesn't negate the possibility of having general reasoning skills, but a great many researchers have missed the point of what form such skills might take and how they might be used. Rather than talk about general reasoning skills, I prefer to talk about general phenomena that occur in the reasoning process.

One such phenomenon is failure. Once again, I am about to advocate something very odd. *Failure should be encouraged.* But here, the schools have taken the opposite path, as usual. This time their reasoning makes superficial sense: The more you succeed, the more you want to succeed. Thus, giving trophies and pats on the back and eliminating discouragement by eliminating failure is the way to make everyone succeed. This idea sounds great, but in practice it creates a real problem.

When people learn, in the everyday sense of learning, what they are doing is gathering up sets of expectations. They learn about people by learning who will say and do what when. They learn about physics— that is, everyday physics—by creating expectations for what happens to balls when they are thrown, rocks when they are dropped, trees when they are battered by wind, snowmen when it gets hot, and so on. We learn about business or law or medicine by gaining experience, and that experience is in the form of expectations about what will happen under certain circumstances. In other words, knowledge is strongly related to prediction. We feel knowledgeable when we feel safe in our predictions about what will happen next, and predictions come from extrapolations from experience. These extrapolations are expectations about what is about to happen based upon what has already happened.

In short, people are bundles of expectations about everything. When these expectations are satisfied, when something happens just the way you thought it would, processing proceeds normally, sentences are parsed, you get what you asked for, your predictions are satisfied. But the news in these situations is not all good. When things happen the way you expected, no learning takes place.

Learning takes place when failures occur. When an expectation fails, when something doesn't go the way we expected, even if we expected not to achieve a goal or unexpectedly succeeded at the goal, we must attempt to explain what happened. Learning, then, is tied up with explanation. When events in the world can be explained by prior events—that is, when standard explanations suffice—learning does not occur. When one is learning, one is learning, among other things, new explanations. One is learning why something happened to be able to make more accurate predictions in the future.

To help in the process of extrapolation from experience, we have the phenomenon of reminding. People commonly find that one situation reminds them of another, quite different situation, and they aren't quite sure why. Often, however, these remindings are linked by having an identical expectation failure and an identical explanation of the expectation failure. In order to think about something in a profound way, drawing upon similar experiences helps. In order to think about related experiences, though, you must be able to find those related experiences. The more remindings we have examined, the more likely that the explanations of expectation failure will be some of the indices that human memory uses to find those related experiences. In other words, when an expectation fails, we explain why to ourselves. That explanation becomes the name in memory of the experience. We remember events in terms of their most significant attributes, and one of the most significant is an expectation that has failed.

But why does reminding occur? One possibility is that the mind recalls relevant data when an expectation failure occurs. You might more easily understand something peculiar if you have additional data and can make a generalization that holds for both. But reminding is also a kind of verification for hypothesized explanations. Once the mind proposes an explanation for an expectation failure, the explanation becomes an index that brings other memories to mind to see whether that explanation relates to anything else in memory.

Reminding is part of a more general process that relates strongly to the issue of general reasoning skills. Often, when you are trying to find an explanation for something, you aren't reminded of anything at all. Or, more accurately, you don't feel that you have been reminded. For example, sometimes when faced with a human problem, you find that a proverb comes to mind. *What should I do? Make hay while the sun shines. A stitch in time saves nine.* Of course, intellectuals don't like to talk this way, but a great many other people do; and intellectuals probably find these proverbs coming to mind even if they don't actually say them.

Similarly, when you confront someone else's problem, you often find yourself thinking of your own previous problem that looked a great deal like the one at hand. And we do tell each other about what we are reminded of. In fact, a great deal of our natural, personal conversations are exchanges of stories, one reminding related to another.

What is the significance of this? A great deal of human reasoning ability is bound up in our ability to find prior reasoning experiences and to relate them to the current situation. The problem with the concept of a general problem solver, something that early AI researchers were trying to build, is that it misses a great deal of what goes on in everyday planning. A more realistic concept of human problem solving might be:

Get reminded of problem like the current one
Tweak

This means that the way we solve problems is by relying upon a repertoire of previously solved problems, cleverly indexed to come to mind at just the right moment. Of course, these problems are not identical to the one being considered at any given moment, so after a fairly relevant problem comes to mind, the issue is to tweak, or modify, it into relevance. In other words, we employ various tricks for getting it to look like the problem at hand, and when we establish the correlation between the two, we have found a candidate explanation. Frequently these candidate explanations are quite silly. One cannot be sure one has found the right initial problem, through reminding, to start tweaking. So, often the issue is how to find another prior problem for tweaking.

A great many important general phenomena occur in the world of specific reasoning skills. One must know how to recharacterize a problem many times in the search for new indices that will yield relevant old problems for current consideration. One must have a storehouse of what we call explanation patterns—that is, good old standards that can be adapted to new situations. These explanations might be as general as proverbs, as specific as one particular experience, or that standard explanation learned in medical school. In the end, however, one must be able to adapt these patterns and make them relevant to situations they don't obviously apply to. Similarly, if we want to teach creativity to children, as we clearly should, then creativity may be a function of having many patterns available, being able to find them when needed, and being able to tweak them into relevance.

Are these general reasoning skills? Of course they are. And in order to be an effective reasoner, one would also have to employ more commonly thought-of general reasoning skills, such as the elimination of candidates by counterexample. These skills, however, rely upon very specific patterns and very specific rules for finding and tweaking those patterns.

My point about LOGO is that teaching general reasoning skills is a laudable goal, but teaching general skills as they apply to a specific area is a more accurate and more relevant goal. Software that allows a child to explore an area of knowledge is important. Software that allows a child to fail is more important. Without failure, a child cannot learn. But all too often, failure in school means bad grades and ridicule from one's peers. What children need is a way to explore, hypothesize, fail, explain, reconsider, and create. In principle, computers do offer this possibility. LOGO is but one realization of an attempt to allow exploration in geometry. LOGO is an important concept, not because geometry is important, but because exploration is important, and recovering from failure is important.

Perhaps the most interesting aspect of a new technology is its acceptance or, more likely, its lack of acceptance by the community at large. The reactions to Papert's attempt to inject exploration into the schools serves as a case in point. Whenever someone is being innovative, you can count on various "experts" to state why the innovation should not be completed. Innovations don't come from thin air. They are made gradually. Therefore, any discussion of whether computers are good or bad for children is a little premature. Nevertheless, since that discussion has been taking place for some time now, we should address the issues so that some wise choices can be made.

The issue is not whether computers are good teaching devices. Any such discussion forces well-meaning critics to talk about the advantages of having a loving, caring, human teacher in a friendly social environment. I am sure that would be very nice—but who has it? The modern classroom? No matter how well-meaning teachers are—and not all of them are, after all, when faced with children who cannot understand what's going on and with those who are bored to death—their attention is spread out sparsely indeed.

And what are the children who are not receiving individual attention doing? If they are doing what they are supposed to, they are going through programmed workbooks or sets of photocopied sheets. They are doing hundreds of problems that they already know how to do and are bored with, but that they must complete to get to the next set of more interesting problems; or they are doing hundreds of problems that they do not understand, and no one is there to explain the problems to them; or, what is more common, they are doing hundreds of problems that are irrelevant, that purport to teach a thing but do not. Schoolchildren are already programmed, in the worst sense of the word. They do what they have to do to get through books that have nothing tailored to their needs and that teach outdated subject matter. Moreover, publishers have no interest in modifying these books even when shown that they do not teach the subject accurately or that they teach something entirely irrelevant.

Critics comment about what kind of child will come out of the computer age. They are concerned that children will be able to relate only to computers. I am concerned that children be educated at all, that they be excited by learning, that they not view their entire school career as preparation for the SATs. I am concerned that they stop being rewarded for the answers and start being rewarded for good questions.

Computers have the potential for changing what is taught in the schools. Why? Reasoning can be taught well in open-ended environments. Reading can be taught that way as well. We can't know how computers will affect children, teachers, and the school curriculum unless we try. Maybe children who learn primarily via a machine will need some clever methods of learning about social interaction when they are not working with the machine. No one is suggesting that all education take place on a computer. The issue is how education can be improved at all. With computers entering the schools in record numbers, education could be improved if the right software were available.

Unfortunately, the book publishers have again played the role of villain, by producing software that supposedly has enhanced their books but in reality simply has put their awful programmed texts on the screen. This is how the situation is, not how it has to be. We need people with tremendous amounts of money who are willing to try educational reform by using computer software. Too often, however, decisions about computers in the schools are made from observations of the software that is currently available.

Why is it so hard to imagine what will be? One hears remarks such as, "Computers have nothing more to do with learning than good spelling has." Such observations merely show a lack of understanding about computers. Learning about computers may be equated with learning about spelling, but computers ought to be related to the invention of books. Having books readily available to children changed education radically. Computers are a medium, not for teaching about computers, but for teaching what one has always taught and what one has not been able to teach for lack of a method to do so.

Of course, most current programs are limited. But what if hundreds of LOGO-like programs were available? Once children have open-ended software that allows them to make hypotheses, they will make hypotheses.

The computers most children have access to right now are not very useful, so I see no great advantage in having them. No jobs will come as a result of learning BASIC in the fourth grade. Computers are becoming cheaper and cheaper, so the problem will not be whether every child can have one. One way or another, most will. The issue is what children will do on computers. How much software are governmental agencies or private foundations developing to which every student will have access? The answer is, not much at all. Right now, with the exception of LOGO and one or two other kinds of open-ended software, nothing very interesting is in the works for children and computers. The solution is to encourage the creation of new software tools that challenge children's minds.

The possibility of creating new software for children brings with it the possibility of changing what is taught to children. Changing anything suddenly, least of all schools, however, is very difficult. We can talk about why mathematics is the wrong subject to teach in school, but the likelihood of quick change in that area, even if all relevant parties were miraculously to agree, is slim. The system is set up to teach mathematics and to gather test scores by using mathematics, changing the system will take years.

Ironically, the real power of computers has nothing to do with computers at all. Since the drive to gather new resources for children, particularly new technological resources, is always strong, acquiring new computer hardware and software will always be far easier to do than, say, eliminating mathematics. (Eliminating is always harder to do than adding in the schools.) The real power of computers, therefore, is in the quick addition of new material to the curriculum. Schools will buy software if many people like it and it doesn't replace anybody. In the near future, the opportunity to create just such software will have arrived.

So, what should children be learning in an ideal world? And can we harness computers to be the medium for teaching whatever that may turn out to be? First, let's consider the question of how one goes about teaching the kinds of things we might want children to do on a computer. Thinking about how you teach computers can help us to see children as something other than little computers themselves.

For example, how would we go about teaching a computer to find the length of the hypotenuse of a right triangle? Basically, two issues are involved. The first is teaching the computer to understand the English used in expressing the question. This is difficult but not really that complicated, because the English in such problems is fairly straightforward. In fact, as long as twenty years ago, some programs could understand algebra word problems far more complicated than that.

The second issue is the formula for answering the question. Anyone with the slightest bit of programming knowledge could put that formula into a computer program in a matter of minutes. Thus equipped, our computer could answer problems about right triangles (no more and no less) endlessly.

What do these issues tell us about education? We can infer that while a child who learns the proper formula is well equipped to handle a problem to which the formula applies, he or she simply does not have to think at all, in any profound sense of the term "think." If we simply want our children to apply ready-made formulas or to spout correct answers, we will end up with very unimaginative young people. I am not against the learning and application of formulas where one might need to know them for some purpose. We should differentiate, however, between the need to know the formula and the need to reason within the subject area.

Learning the official rules of the game doesn't always help when it comes to reality. Reasoning by reminding, as opposed to reasoning by applying formulas, can be a very valuable tool in everyday life. For example, let's take a familiar case of real-life reasoning. Suppose you were asked which candidate for president was most likely to make peace: the sabre-rattling hawk or the let's-withdraw-the-troops liberal? You might respond that the question reminded you of Richard Nixon. You might argue that he was virulently anti-Communist, but yet the first to go to China. You might reason that candidates tend to do the opposite of what they say. This thought might remind you that Lyndon Johnson was the peace candidate during the early stages of the Vietnam War.

Reasoning by reminding is something that must be taught in the schools. How and where should we do this? In math class? In history class? In philosophy class? We actually do teach this method of thought in some cases. Professional mathematicians prove theorems by relying upon prior theorems and adapting them to the new situation. We should do the same in math class instead of teaching formulas. Of course, some wise teachers do use prior cases to teach, but they teach the formulas as well. Forget the formulas; teach examples, and teach children how to reason from examples.

Law schools and business schools follow the celebrated Harvard case method. Must children wait until professional school to learn how to think? Let's teach first-graders how to survive in the streets and how to make a choice in an election. I do not mean let's teach the *facts* in these situations. There are no facts. Rather, teach children about the prior cases, and teach them to build on those cases to reason about new ones. Children already know how to do this, of course, since, as I have said, this method is fundamental to normal human thought processes. What do we have to teach the children, then? We must teach them that this method of reasoning is all right. We must teach them baseline cases to rely upon in different areas of knowledge. In the graduate schools at Harvard, that's what students are learning: They are learning the cases and how to reason from them. Cases can be taught in any subject area at any time. Why not start in first grade?

The reliance on formulaic thought is quite dangerous, as I have noted. If a computer simply learned a rule and applied it, none of us would be convinced that a computer was smart. We don't confer the honor of intelligence so easily. A computer would have to do something much more complex than apply a formula in the right situation and come up with the right answer to convince us of its intelligence. It would have to come up with the formula on its own or, at least, arrive at some insight on its own. Why, then, do we demand less of children, who have considerably more native intelligence than computers do?

Children should not be considered intelligent simply for learning the formula, any more than computers should be. Children can be taught to invent the formula or to reason about a class of similar problems. My view of teaching formulas? Teach children what a formula is, but never teach them a formula. Let them invent $E = mc^2$ on their own. Impossible? Not really. The trick to real invention, of the kind Einstein did, is to be asking the right questions. If we present children with the right questions, deriving the formula will be comparatively easy for them.

These arguments do not apply solely to mathematics, of course. We observe a great many rules, such as the Pythagorean theorem, in daily life. These rules are called proverbs or clichés, depending on their presumed profundity. So, when a person takes vitamins every day, he may, consciously or unconsciously, be living by the rule "An ounce of prevention is worth a pound of cure." Or when a child walks away from people who are taunting him, he may yell back, "sticks and stones may break my bones, but names will never hurt me." "Rules" such as these govern much of our lives, and following rules is neither right nor wrong. At times, these rules form perfectly sound advice. The problem for the creative thinker is recognizing when there are no rules available or when the available rules are, for some reason, inappropriate.

Obviously, the reason to learn a formula is the same as that for writing a computer program to follow a formula. Learning a formula is important to the extent that we employ repetitive procedures and to the extent that we need to use a formula again and again. But, of course, in the computer age, even that need has vanished. We can find little justification for learning any formula as long as machines exist that can slavishly do these computations for us.

Exceptions arise, of course. Having hand calculators available is no reason for failing to learn to add. Why? Because we need to understand first principles in order to reason for ourselves. In order to reason by asking, we must have at our disposal the basic questions to ask. In other words, we must know how to add in order to understand multiplication, we must understand multiplication in order to understand division, and so on. A formula is not a basic tool of asking. It introduces no new concepts, but merely applies old ones.

Schools have been teaching formulas for a long time now. In the computer age, teaching children to do what computers can do makes little sense. Rather, we must teach children to do what computers cannot do. If in some years, the achievements of computers equal those of our children, if creative thought becomes formulaic in nature, then, at least, the equation of people with computers will be on a higher plane than it is now.

How, then, do we teach creative reasoning? The first thing we have to do is to get over the idea that questions have right answers. In school, we expect answers to questions. We want facts. We ask who discovered America, and we want the name Columbus, not some hedging about Vikings or comments about Native Americans. We are a fact-oriented society. Schools, as they are presently constituted in the United States, have one primary purpose educationally—the effective performance of their students on standardized tests.

Clearly, schools have other functions, such as keeping kids off the street, providing a mechanism for social assimilation, teaching children a common set of facts about the world, and introducing students to the need to get along within a bureaucracy—that is, school itself. Underlying all of these functions should be the ability to reason and to think. This clear and unifying focus is usually lost in the attempt to score well on tests.

Children are taught from the very early grades that right answers do exist and that they will be rewarded for getting as many right answers as possible. What should we do? We should learn about what it means to think. Schools cannot teach thinking if they don't know what it means or how to do it.

Maxim 1: Teach Questions, not Answers. Probably the most significant thing one can say about thinking is that it is inspired by questions. In many cases, these questions can come from the real needs of everyday life. So, if one is frequently asked questions, or if one frequently comes upon unusual situations that pose problems, one will get lots of practice in thinking.

The school situation could be an acceptable format for the asking of questions, but as long as formulaic answers satisfy the questions, then the questions are not of any use. Further, questions with one and only one right answer are of no use in stimulating thinking. To think, one must learn to justify one's answers in front of a severe and respected critic. This can be your spouse, a teacher, or even your child, but it must be someone who is willing to argue with you. You must be able to justify your answer. If you cannot, you have not answered the question.

Learning to think in a creative, stimulating fashion requires learning to be inquisitive. Specifically:

1. You must be asked questions, by either yourself, others, or situations you encounter.

2. These questions must be out of the ordinary. If you have been asked the same question before, so that answering it requires no more than mentally looking up the answer, the question won't help you think.

3. Someone whom you respect must evaluate your answer.

Could a computer follow this procedure? Who, or what, could do it better? A nonjudgmental teacher before whom one could fail without embarrassment would be pleasant to have. Let computers allow children to hypothesize.

Maxim 2: Socrates Was Right. What goes on in a physics course? The student learns lots of formulas and rules and learns to recognize when to apply which formula. If a laboratory is associated with the course, the student gets an opportunity to observe that the formulas are pretty accurate, except, of course, if the student makes a mistake.

Then the formula still must be correct, and the student knows that her experimental technique is poor—and so will be her grade, most likely. What do students learn? They learn to *reason by rule application.* As I have argued above, this approach to thinking is basic, but limited. What the student does not learn is to be creative. The problem-solving paradigm obviates creativity. Furthermore, this approach to teaching science has a fundamental premise that is unfounded and even damaging—namely, that scientists know what the right answer is. This assumption of correctness and precision in physics and other sciences is very misleading and is readily questioned by actual practitioners. The idea that all the answers are known is more horrifying yet. But students actually believe this about physics, about psychology, about . . . you name it. Why do they believe it? Because no matter how many times good teachers might deny that they know all the answers, they still teach as if they do. Teachers have to if they give exams with the usual questions and answers on them. In many ways, exams—especially standardized exams, which are easy to grade because all the answers are precisely one thing or another— are the true villains.

An alternative can be found in a literature or philosophy course. In these fields, the notion of a right answer has largely been discarded. What is the right interpretation of *Hamlet?* What is freedom? What can be known? Philosophers often delight in arguing the same question from two opposing points of view—or three or four or five. The archetype of this style of reasoning is Socrates. Socrates gave his students not answers, but questions. In doing so, he taught them how to ask questions themselves and how to think.

Discussion-based teaching has become widely accepted in English, history, and other humanities. In these fields, teachers are much less concerned about the "student learning problem," and this is not merely a coincidence. The interactive nature of discussions provides the student with greater involvement in the material and, most important, with intrinsic motivation. The problem-solving paradigm typical of physics is more remote.

Imagine, then, a Socratic dialogue about physics. The teacher would not be there to write a proof on the blackboard demonstrating the veracity of some formula. The instructor would raise questions about physical phenomena and would stimulate the students to ask questions of their own. Students shouldn't be handed the accepted wisdom without understanding why it is important in the first place. To them, the question should be, Why does the world behave in this way? The subject matter should stimulate students to investigate and ask more questions rather than to provide merely extrinsic goals that prompt them to ask, Is this going to be on the exam?

Great, but how do you teach students to ask questions? This question may not have an answer, but it's a good question. (I say this to my graduate students all the time in class—they hate it when I do.) How can computers teach students to ask questions? Computers can become mere presenters of information. Let the machines know a lot, and have them say what they know at appropriate times. This would be the ultimate in Socratic teaching—a machine that never interjects its own opinion because it has no opinion. It knows only some cases it can tell you about when it hears you thinking about something related.

Maxim 3: Force Students to Create Hypotheses. What we ask of our computer teacher is to stimulate the student to ask questions. The basic cycle for the interaction would be:

1. Computer poses a difficult question, which may have no right answer.

2. Student generates a hypothesis.

3. Computer responds with a counterexample from its data base of remindings.

Then, the student must revise the hypothesis, and the cycle continues. Note that a central part of this process is that the student fails to get the right answer. The computer is continually trying to point out holes in the student's answers. A computer can get away with this, whereas a teacher in a classroom cannot. The reason is simple but compelling: The computer is not judgmental. Children are sensitive to the attitudes of teachers and other students. No child wants to be continually singled out as unable to answer a question. The computer has greater latitude. Its interaction is private. Other students aren't aware of the mistakes that any one child has made. Neither is the teacher. Computers offer students a great and important luxury: the opportunity to fail. Our educational system can capitalize on this underlying cognitive mechanism by, in effect, providing opportunities for the child to make mistakes and fail without the stigma normally associated with negative reinforcement. Computers provide a one-on-one teaching environment free from the intimidating effects of public scrutiny.

People rely on experience to understand new situations and to provide predictions that can be applied to new cases. Sometimes a prediction does not work—that is, the world does not always behave in the way you expect it to behave. These expectation failures provide an opportunity for learning by stimulating the person to explain what went wrong. The explanations can be used to locate other experiences that may be related. The explanation and associated remindings are then incorporated into the knowledge base of prediction and help to prevent the person from repeating the failure.

Maxim 4: Students Should Discover Answers. Computers have arrived in classrooms across the country amid very high expectations. In the past twenty years, we have witnessed dramatic and exciting developments in computer hardware, which have resulted in the wide availability of powerful machines at a small fraction of the cost of the decades before. These new computers were going to change the way children were taught and start a revolution in learning.

Most of the learning from computers that has occurred is by the teachers and administrators who have realized that computers are not living up to their early promise. Computers have not transformed the schools into technological forums of learning. The schools are still having a hard time teaching the bread-and-butter subjects of reading, writing, and arithmetic. The only subject that absolutely requires the use of a computer is learning about the computer itself—hardly a surprising result.

What should computers be doing in the classroom, then? Computers make it possible to learn through simulations. The user can make decisions that change the state of an imaginary world. The child becomes more involved in the action and has to think about his decisions and their consequences. In this environment, the child can experiment with impunity. This approach can be applied to the entire school curriculum—not simply for math problems or spelling drills. A history program could allow the student to simulate political decisions and view events occurring in a causal sequence. A geography program might let the child explore a region and discover its traditions, economy, and so on. A student might manipulate the economy of a country at a micro or macro level and discover the underlying explanations for consumer decisions and national fiscal policies. A computer chemistry lab would allow the student not only to perform experiments for qualitative and quantitative analysis but also to manipulate molecular models of the results. A biology program could perform (and, in some pilot projects, can perform) simulated genetics experiments instantly without waiting the few days required for real fruit fly results.

The educational process must revise its treatment of the whole idea of failure. The age-old methods merely punish failure to understand and terminate learning. We have to create a learning environment that leads a student who has failed to understand something to want honestly to know what he has misunderstood.

A computer running an interactive learning program could provide just such a learning environment. Computer-based learning can enhance the ability to fail easily and the ability to question and explore the knowledge that would have permitted success. Computers don't ridicule you for failure. You can come up with a weird hypothesis, a crazy explanation, a half-baked idea more easily if you know that a computer is going to respond to it. This assertion assumes, however, that you have available a computer that is intelligent or, at least, intelligently programmed.

The same is true of asking questions. A person might think you were stupid for asking a question, but a computer never would. A student will more willingly risk making a mistake in the simulated world of the computer environment: if no real mistake is made, no real disaster can follow, and you have no one to answer to but yourself.

Explanations, questions, reminding, hypothesis making, and generalization are at the heart of the learning process. The above principles of learning and understanding, together with the glaring faults in the current educational system, lead to a set of maxims that should embody both the goals of education and the design goals of school curriculums and educational software.

Maxim 5: Teach (that is, Encourage) Students to Create Explanations, Not to Accept Explanations. The ability to explain why something has occurred is a fundamentally important intellectual process. Creativity depends upon our ability to think up new explanations for phenomena we don't understand. Why people act the way they do, why institutions do what they do, why the physical world behaves the way it does—these are all subjects of creative inquiry. They are also the kinds of things most people think about during a given day. When someone tells us what to think, we tend to accept the explanation and not to create our own. But without such help, we do create our own explanations. In fact, we do so quite easily.

Maxim 6: Teach Students to Reason by Reminding, Not by Formula Application. Schools love to teach formulas. After all, the formulas exist to be memorized, don't they? And tests based upon formulas are so easy to grade. But of what value are the formulas? Do we really need to compute the hypotenuse of a right triangle? How often does this question come up in daily life? Formulas are interesting only because they capture generalizations. Shouldn't we be teaching children to capture generalizations on their own, then? How can we do that? By teaching children to *reason by reminding*. Reasoning by reminding is a natural process that needs to be reemphasized more than taught. We are reminded of one thing by another all the time. Our minds use these remindings to help us form generalizations. A generalization is a kind of hypothesis. In other words, people naturally create hypotheses on the basis of their own experiences, but when we teach these same people mathematics, we teach them to memorize the hypotheses of others rather than to create hypotheses of their own. If the hypotheses they learn are useful only for computing hypotenuses, then something is wrong.

Maxim 7: The Proper Subjects for Study Are the Cases Themselves, Not the Rules that Have Been Abstracted from Those Cases. You cannot create hypotheses unless you have had some experience in the matters you wish to speculate about. If you have had two experiences, you can compare them and form a generalization that links them. If you have had ten related experiences, your generalizations are likely to be somewhat more accurate. What does this tell us about education? We must teach cases. Education depends upon having many experiences. "Experience is the greatest teacher" may not be an innovative idea, but it is an idea that is happily ignored in most schools.

Maxim 8: Know What the Questions Are, Not What the Answers Are. The ability to think depends upon the ability to come up with good questions. You learn more easily when you really want to know about something. In other words, the easiest way to learn something is to be curious about it, to develop a question about it before you hear the answer. We should be teaching questioning, not answering.

Maxim 9: Engage Students in Dialogues About Subjects They Don't Understand. If you want to find out about something, it helps to ask. But people are often afraid to ask. They don't want to be found out. They are afraid people will think they are stupid. Children are afraid other children will laugh at them; adults, that their boss will lose respect for them. Too bad about this, since dialogue about what you don't understand is what teaching is all about.

Maxim 10: Encourage Students to Make Hypotheses About Subjects They Don't Understand. Learning means thinking and questioning. All this should result in a hypothesis. Which is better: To be told that $F=ma$?

Or to have been wondering about why Johnny punches harder than Jimmy and, in attempting to figure it out, discovering that F=ma?

Maxim 11: Encourage the Discovery of Answers by Experimentation with Hypotheses. Of course, your initial hypotheses may be wrong. What then? Test them out, and try again. Great scientists work like this. Why not students?

The Questionable Reality of Media

JOSHUA MEYROWITZ

Metaphors are potent and valuable thinking tools. They help us to see clearly. But they also blind us to alternative views. Once we fasten on one metaphor for a phenomenon, it becomes difficult to think of the phenomenon as anything other than that metaphor.

What are "media"? The question seems too simple to deserve a serious answer. Although media are commonly thought to alter the reality of various social phenomena—politics, socialization, education, gender roles, the level of social violence, and so on—the reality of media is generally seen as unproblematic. It is agreed that media *do* certain things, but for many observers, media themselves simply *are*. Their nature is apparently too transparent to require massive discussion and analysis.

Ironically, the variety of possible conceptions of media is obscured by their commonness. In the United States, 98 percent of households have televisions, 96 percent have telephones. Radios outnumber people. And hardly anyone has had no experiences with books, magazines, newspapers, photographs, movies, VCRs, and computers. Such media are so familiar that it seems almost unnecessary to articulate our mental constructs of them. We accept their presence in our lives matter-of-factly, as we accept the windows of our homes or the members of our families.

Yet as with all observations of the world, our conceptions of media are themselves mediated by mental constructs. As with other attempts to comprehend complex phenomena, we rely, often subconsciously, on metaphorical thinking to simplify and clarify what media are.

Metaphors are potent and valuable thinking tools. They help us to see clearly. But they also blind us to alternative views. Once we fasten on one metaphor for a phenomenon, it becomes difficult to think of the phenomenon as anything other than that metaphor. As linguist George Lakoff and philosopher Mark Johnson have suggested, for example, a pervasive metaphor in the United States is that argument is war. [1] We "defend" positions; "win" or "lose" arguments; "counterattack"; "demolish" a criticism; "shoot down" evidence; provide an "on-target" response; and so on. Recent support for Lakoff and Johnson came from George Bush, who, while running for the presidency, compared his on-camera argument with TV news anchor Dan Rather to his combat experiences in World War II.

Yet argument is not, in fact, war, though we may often treat it as such. There are many other potential conceptions of argument. One could think of argument as play (the Talmudic tradition of argument has a strong playful element). Australians, it is said, are more likely than Americans to use argument to signal respect and interest in developing a friendship.[2] And I have one old friend who views, and uses, argument as a form of seduction.

Metaphors guide thought and action. Jacob Bronowski has described how Isaac Newton was able to use a simple image, that of the moon as a ball thrown around the earth so hard and fast that it would never land, to generate a complex theory of physics. In a darker example, Robert Jay Lifton suggests that metaphor played a role in the atrocities committed by Nazi doctors: The disease metaphor allowed doctors to see themselves as removing sickly organs and limbs in order to save the body politic. Thus they saw themselves serving society and fulfilling their medical oath to protect life, even as they maimed and killed.[3]

While reliance on metaphors is not inherently bad or good in a moral sense, it is also not epistemologically neutral. Metaphors are necessary for most clear thinking and action, but for better and for worse, they also shape thought and behavior into particular patterns that mistakenly come to be seen as flowing from natural, direct perception.

An examination of metaphorical thinking about media would be a worthy goal even if there were general cultural consensus as to what media are (that is, consensus on what metaphorical frame to apply to them). It is even more important when competing—but often implicit—metaphors operate silently and simultaneously, leaving us confused as to what we know about media.

Metaphors are rampant in thinking and writing on media, but they often are treated either as objective descriptions of the "reality" of media or as simple "figures of speech" that have aesthetic but not perceptual consequences. Different metaphors, however, encourage people to see different things when they examine media.

Television alone has been called by a multitude of names, including window on the world, boob tube, glass teat, electronic fireplace, new language, friend, tabula rasa, painkiller, new state religion, neutral channel, hypnotist, salesperson, political arena, white noise, escape hatch, plug-in drug, electronic wallpaper, marketplace, town crier, thief of time, Big Brother, our eyes and ears, pulpit, cultivator, agenda setter, entertainer, vast wasteland, anthology of texts, network of social relations, baby-sitter, teacher, liberator, instrument of terror, and nineteen-inch neighborhood. Similar arrays of metaphors permeate discussions of the movies, radio, books, photography, computers, and other media.

Although a vast array of implicit and explicit metaphors exists in analyses of media, my contention is that virtually all the questions and statements about any medium, or about media in general, can be related to one of three central metaphors for what a medium of communication is: medium as a vessel or conduit, medium as a language, medium as a setting or environment. An examination of these core metaphors involves pushing aside for the moment the diverse surface concerns that critics, researchers, and average citizens have about media and asking, What are the major underlying conceptions of the reality of media?

MEDIUM AS VESSEL/CONDUIT

The most common media metaphor is that a medium is a vessel or a conduit. The vessel/conduit metaphor looks at media as holding or sending important "stuff" that deserves attention and analysis. This leads to a variety of ways of studying the "content" of media. The particular medium (radio, newspaper, television, and so on) is seen as a neutral conveyor.

Broadly speaking, the vessel/conduit metaphor leads one to ask:

What is the content? How did the content get there? How do people interpret the content? What effects does the content have?

The vessel/conduit image is widely shared. It is the metaphor whispered or shouted from a thousand lips in a thousand contexts: the letters to the editor complaining about the content of a newspaper story; the minister's condemnation of television programming; the women's movement's attacks on sexist media content; the movie reviewer's plot summaries; and the millions of dollars worth of research on television violence.

This metaphor is so common because content is the most obvious part of our interactions with media. It is the essence we react to most immediately and most explicitly. We all have a sense that a message that someone loves us has power and meaning apart from whether we receive it in face-to-face interaction, by letter, by phone, by audiotape, or by videotape. Each of those conveyors is different, but we still react to the message first. Few would dispute that a message of love is different from a message of hate, regardless of how it is conveyed.

Within the vessel/conduit metaphor, content is "medium-free"; it is that part of the overall message that is separable in some way from its particular presentation in a particular medium. While this is a limited notion of content, it has experiential reality. Many people are concerned about media violence, sexism, and sexuality irrespective of the medium that contains them. Indeed, much mainstream media research and criticism falls into these areas. And we should be troubled by government disinformation, whether it reaches us through public speeches, radio, television, or newspaper.

Similarly, we have a sense that a movie can be made from a book, or that one can transcribe an interview and somehow retain the "same interview."[4] These examples suggest that we perceive some essence that can be transported unchanged from medium to medium.

If you miss your favorite television program and you ask a friend to tell you what happened, generally what you hear about is the content. You might learn, for example, that the sexy wife of a rich white industrialist has been kidnapped for ransom and taken to a warehouse. The kidnappers are two strong, but ignorant, black men, and their white boss is a bitter, slightly crazed past employee of the industrialist who was hurt in a factory accident and is now confined to a wheelchair. The kidnapped woman is a housewife who has spent most of her adult life in the kitchen, and she now unthinkingly adopts her kidnappers as her new family. She cooks them three meals a day . . . and they all live happily ever after.

This description includes many important elements. It tells us much about the negative and stereotyped portrayal of women, blacks, and the disabled in the story. (Note again how easy it is to accept that an oral description—as well as my written account of it here—is capable of conveying the nature of a *televised* story.) But this description does not tell us much about any particular medium or about media per se.

Of course, analysis of content can be much more sophisticated than a friend's description of a missed show. One can look beyond manifest content to the underlying structure or form of the content. For example, one can look at genres, at unconscious or psychoanalytic motivations of producers of content, at implicit value systems, at the ways in which news and entertainment narratives are shaped by media industry structure and by economic and political forces, at broader cultural meanings that swirl through media content, or at the ways in which interpretations of messages vary from person to person and from group to group. One can examine correlations between media content and reality, explore the effects of content, or consider the types of messages that rarely if ever appear in mainstream media. Content data can also be quantified and analyzed statistically.

But even in these more complex approaches, one is still looking primarily at the content, rather than at the medium through which the content is delivered. The medium is viewed as significant only insofar as people receive its content. Television content, for example, is one of the most popular subjects of study simply because almost every American household owns at least one television set. Within this metaphor, the workings of the television/conduit—the ways in which it uniquely packages and delivers its messages—are generally ignored. The content of television is often examined in the same way that the content of comics or novels or movies would be. The particular medium is viewed as a neutral delivery system.

MEDIUM AS LANGUAGE

A very different metaphor is that each medium is a particular language. The language metaphor looks at every medium as having a unique range of expressive potential. This leads to the study of the "grammar" (or production variables) *within* each medium and how its manipulation alters the resulting message—even when basic content elements, such as those discussed above, remain unchanged.

Broadly speaking, grammar questions ask: What variables can be manipulated within each medium? What are the roots of the grammatical code—both within the nature of the medium and in the structural codes of face-to-face communication? What are the effects of such manipulations in terms of perception, comprehension, emotional reaction, and behavioral response?

In print media, production variables include size and style of type, texture of paper, color of type and paper, use of white space, and arrangements of the mosaic of each page. In photography, grammar variables include the shape and aspect ratio of the frame, camera angle, selection of focus, depth of focus, shot framing from close-up to long shot, and focal length of the lens (which affects the degree of compression/elongation of background and foreground). In audio production, variables include pickup patterns of microphones (roughly analogous to wide angle versus telephoto lenses), frequency filters, multitracking, and so forth. Television and film incorporate all the variables of still photography and audio, plus such variables as dissolves, fades, cutting speed, zooms, dollies, tilts, pans, and changes in focus.

Unlike content elements, which are often identical to behaviors that take place in nonmediated interactions, grammar questions focus on variables that are particular to media. While one can exhibit violence or sexism in real life, for example, it is difficult to "cut to a close-up" or "dissolve to the beach" in everyday interactions. And one cannot change typefaces in speech.

Of course, grammar variables may have rough physical and psychological correlates in face-to-face communication. Shot structure may be related to situationally and culturally variant speaking distances and to real-life "angles" (as when a child cranes his or her neck to look up to a parent).[5] But the actual production variables remain unique means of expression within a particular medium or type of media (all visual media, for example, have a number of similar variables).

The language metaphor is most prevalent among those involved in the actual production of various media, and among critics and researchers with some training in production techniques. Among media, film enjoys the highest proportion of analyses based at least in part on the language metaphor, perhaps because critics and theorists often watch a film more than once (thereby becoming more aware of the grammatical manipulations), perhaps because filmmakers generally spend more time than producers of other media in constructing and perfecting the grammar of their productions.

Grammar variables are more difficult to perceive than content variables. You can find them if you concentrate on looking for them, but it usually is difficult to focus on them and pay attention to the content at the same time. If, for example, you are watching television and you begin to concentrate on shot selection, mood music, and camera angles, you usually find it difficult to follow the story as well. You have to watch a show several times to take it all in. The average viewer will feel pity during the kidnapping of the industrialist's wife in the content example, and will *not* say: "Wow, what an interesting camera angle," or "I'm glad the director used that tight close-up; it really grabbed me!"

Producers do not particularly want average consumers of media forms to be aware of the role of grammar. Newspapers rarely acknowledge the role that typeface and layout play in establishing their image and level of credibility. Television news programs do not highlight the grammatical conventions that give news sequences a documentary rather than fictional tone. Indeed, producers often consider it part of their professional responsibility to *hide* the production techniques that have impact apart from the content. The artist often hopes the viewer will simply feel the appropriate emotion as if it is the only reasonable reaction to the story (content). Yet such directorial decisions are very significant in terms of creating all images and stereotypes in television and film.

My students are often surprised to discover that the way one knows who the "main character" is in a movie has at least as much to do with grammar as with content elements. The main character is almost always the first person seen in prolonged close-ups. Close-ups thrust a character into vicarious intimate space. Choice of shots and angles is often more important than the content elements in defining the intensity of response. When you watch television, for example, you may notice that you rarely have a particularly strong response—either negative or positive—to characters who are shown only in long shots. Unless you see characters in medium shots or close-ups, you usually respond to them only in terms of the social role they are portraying (secretary, jury member, soldier, and so on). This is one of the reasons why we do not get very upset every time a soldier gets killed in a war movie, and why we may become very upset when "our character" is even slightly wounded.

Another significant production variable in television and film is the use of subjective and objective shots. An objective shot is one that shows the action from an outsider's perspective. A subjective shot, however, shows people and events as one of the characters within the action sees them. The use of subjective shots, in effect, gives the viewer a perception of a perception (somewhat analogous to first-person narrative in novels), and we tend to feel a natural empathy with the person whose perspective we see. Of course, even objective shots are hardly neutral, since they provide a predetermined perspective, in a sense creating a character for us as a particular observer and judge.

In the story about the kidnapping of the industrialist's wife, selective use of close-ups and manipulation of objective and subjective shots could recast the story in several ways. We might, for example, see the disabled kidnapper from an objective low angle that makes him seem powerful and menacing. If this view of him is constant throughout, we may see him as manipulating the woman and continue to dislike him even as she grows fond of him. On the other hand, we might see him only as the woman sees him: first as the major threat and source of evil in the drama, and then as the object of growing affection. (For example, we might eventually see him looking up to the camera plaintively—the image of him that she sees as she stands over his wheelchair.) Or we might see much of the action from *his* perspective (including, perhaps, a subjective flashback of the accident), encouraging us to empathize with his attempt at sweet revenge.

Even in this simpleminded episode, the potential combinations of variables and effects are almost infinite, especially when we take into account the other characters. The manner in which the industrialist is portrayed, for example, will affect the extent to which we empathize with his situation. Similarly, close-ups of the two black henchmen will focus our attention on them as people and make us think about their motives for participating in the kidnapping. A dominance of long shots of the black men, however, will maintain them as mere background characters and focus our thoughts on the triad of white characters: industrialist, wife, and former employee. Yet if the majority of close-ups are of the industrialist and the disabled kidnapper, then the woman will be presented more as a pawn in a power struggle between the two men.

Such variations in shot distance, angle, and subjectivity are almost always used to encourage us to take sides in war movies and westerns, and even in news and documentaries. In most war movies, the camera places us next to "our boys." We stand in their midst; the other side fires at us. We rarely see prolonged close-ups of the enemy (in *Star Wars*, for example, the enemy soldiers and their leader are masked, in *Platoon*, the Viet Cong are mostly fleeting shadows). Such manipulations explain, in large part, the very different response we have to the "criminals" (a content label) in such movies as *The Godfather* and *The Untouchables*. Similarly, many American viewers I know appreciated the quality of the movie *Das Boot*—which thrust viewers into a World War II German submarine—but left the theater uncomfortable with their close identification with the German U-boat crew.

In concerns about sexist portrayals on television, we ought to be as interested in the grammar as in the content. Does the shot structure tend to portray the vision of one sex more than another (as when it shows a man turning his head and then cuts to a woman's behind)? Are women who are portrayed in liberated roles (a content issue) still shown in shots that highlight their sexuality and "delicacy" (as when special filters and tight closeups are used to create a sexual aura)?

Content and grammar elements usually work in tandem to reinforce a consonant perception. Films that portray mindless females and powerful males will often shoot the females in level or slightly high-angle shots (literally looking down on the women and making them appear weak and small), while males are more likely to be shown in low angles, making them appear tall and powerful.

But content and grammar can work against each other as well. Following the 1976 election, for example, *Newsweek* featured a cover story on president-elect Jimmy Carter called "Taking Charge," but the cover photo pictured him from an unflattering high angle that made him look weak and ineffectual. Similarly, one could, theoretically, make a movie about a hospital in which all the doctors are white and all the janitors are black (a content decision); yet if all the close-ups were of the janitors, then the doctors would remain a cluster of background characters and the janitors would become salient personalities. The unlikelihood that a major movie would be shot in this way in the United States today is as much evidence of racial and class bias as any content issue. Changes in shot structure can transform object into subject and vice versa.

Within the language metaphor, the focus remains on variables internal to each medium. The content is examined primarily to the extent to which it can be shaped or altered by manipulation of the medium's grammar, and little or no attention is paid to what is constant about each medium regardless of how its production variables are manipulated.

MEDIUM AS SETTING/ENVIRONMENT

The third media metaphor pictures a medium as a setting or environment. The setting/environment metaphor looks at each medium as a particular type of "context" with characteristics and effects that transcend variations in content and manipulations of production variables.

Broadly speaking, this metaphor leads one to ask: What are the relatively fixed characteristics of a medium? How do these characteristics make it physically, psychologically, and sociologically different from other media, regardless of content and grammar choices?

The notion of media contexts does not refer merely to looking at media "in context"—that is, in terms of the larger political, economic, and social context. (The larger social context can be related to all three media metaphors, and is most often examined in terms of sources and effects of media content within the vessel/conduit metaphor.) Rather, the idea is that each medium itself is a physical and social context that influences behavior and social structure in some way. Context questions always involve an implicit or explicit comparison between one medium and another or between a medium and nonmediated interaction.

Contextual variables of media include the following:

- *The type of sensory information* the medium can and cannot transmit (visual, aural, olfactory, and so on)
- *The form of information* the medium conveys (this differs from sensory information in that aural information could be either dots and dashes or voice, visual information could be either words on a page or images)
- *The speed and degree of immediacy* of communication (how quickly messages can be encoded, sent, and received; how quickly feedback can be sent and received)
- *Unidirectional versus bidirectional* (in contrast to the telephone, for example, broadcast radio and television are primarily unidirectional, in that feedback by the listener is rare and, when existent, indirect and limited)
- *Simultaneous or sequential interaction* (on the telephone, for example, you can hear the other person sigh or comment as you speak, whereas on a CB radio, speakers must take turns communicating)
- *The relative ease or difficulty of learning to use the medium* to code and decode messages and whether one tends to learn to use the medium

all at once, in a few simple steps, or in a prolonged series of stages (it is more difficult to learn to read and write, for example, than it is to learn to speak into and listen to a tape recorder)

- *The physical requirements for using the medium* (for example, whether you have to sit still or are able to move around; whether you have to stop what you are doing to convey a message, as in writing, or whether the medium simply captures a version of what you are saying or doing, as with a camcorder; the extent to which a situation is altered by mediating it, as with an electronic flash for photography)
- *The scope and nature of dissemination* of the mediated communication (How long can it last? How far can it travel? How many and what type of people are likely to have access to it?)

Context questions operate on two levels: the micro, or individual, level and the macro, or societal, level. On the micro level, the contextual issue is how the choice of one medium over another affects a particular situation or interaction. On the macro level, contextual questions explore the ways in which the addition of a medium to the existing media matrix may alter social structure and social interactions in general.

On the micro level, for example, there is a big difference between choosing a telephone call and a letter to extricate yourself from an intimate relationship. On the phone, your verbal message may be overwhelmed by your emotional vocal overtones, and you are interrupted by the words and sounds of the other person. Additionally, you often convey a hesitant and rambling phone message; you cannot completely "erase" what you have said thus far and start again. A "Dear John telephone call" is inherently paradoxical. Since the telephone offers vocal, bidirectional, and simultaneous communication, it maintains an informal, intimate, and fluid relationship, even as you try to end such a relationship.

A Dear John letter, however, allows you to strip away your vocalizations and "have your say" without any interruption or response from the other party. Further, the contextual nature of letter writing allows the sender to write and rewrite a letter until it has a formal and polished form.

On the macro level, those who use the setting/environment metaphor might study the telephone by asking questions such as how its use alters the texture of social relationships in general, affects the speed and style of business interactions, changes the frequency and function of letter writing, and restructures the boundaries of psychological versus physical neighborhoods.[6]

On the micro level, one might ask how the presence of a camera or microphone affects the behavior of a particular politician in a particular situation. On the macro level, one might ask how electronic media alter political styles and, eventually, our perception of politicians in general.[7]

On the micro level, a parent might decide whether to turn on the television set during dinner, not knowing what will appear before his or her children. A related macro-level question would be how television tends to erode the traditional insularity of childhood.[8]

Additional sample macro context questions include these: How does the form in which information is encoded (picture versus word, for example) affect patterns of access, perception, believability, social thought processes, and so on? How do the coding and other characteristics of a medium affect the social balance of information among people of different ages, physical locations, sexes, and levels of education? How and why political and economic elites have fostered the development of some media contexts, while discouraging others (unidirectional broadcast television on a national scale, for example, is more suited to mass persuasion than are interactive and community-based television contexts). How do the contexts fostered by the current media matrix affect other social contexts, such as government, schools, business, and so forth? How do new media alter the use and impact of older media? How do media contexts affect perceptions of appropriate content and grammar choices? (The preference for close-ups in many programs, for example, may be related to the low resolution of our present television system. Similarly, the intimate nature of TV close-ups seems to have fostered a trend away from formal, stadium-style political speeches.)

Context is the least common media metaphor, perhaps because the contextual aspects of media are as elusive as they are pervasive. Contexts are the least visible aspects of media; one cannot see the medium's context in the message or in the manipulations of production variables. Context questions tend to look at issues that are difficult to test and quantify through "social scientific" methods. On the macro level especially, context issues concern large-scale structural changes over long periods of time. Such changes cannot be measured easily through surveys, experiments, or observational research.

Yet context questions may be the most significant for understanding social change and for comparing and contrasting cultural systems. The context metaphor leads to a unique type of question, a question that probes the workings of social behavior in a more complicated manner than simple imitation, persuasion, or attitude change based on content and grammar.

The characteristics of books and television, for example, are sufficiently different that the same content has markedly different effects in each medium. For instance, both books and television may contain advice for parents on what to tell or not to tell children of various ages. But because young children cannot read, and because books are individual objects that can be selectively given to or withheld from children, books allow much more easily for all-adult interactions without children's "overhearing." With the help of such advice books, parents can keep children in the dark about certain matters, and keep them in the dark about being kept in the dark. The same content on a television talk show, however, is likely to have a completely different effect, because thousands of children may be listening in, learning about the very topics that are being recommended for secrecy, as well as learning about the "secret of secrecy"—the fact that adults are concerned about what to tell and not to tell children.

Similarly, in terms of the television show on the industrialist's kidnapped wife, the setting/environment metaphor would not immediately lead to the assumption that sexist and racist content, however offensive it might be, automatically enhances sexism and racism in society. A contextual view of sexism would involve looking not at the content, but at the ways in which each *medium* of communication affects the balance of gender and race roles. Sexist content in one medium might reinforce sexism, while sexist content in another medium might undermine it.

A contextual perspective might suggest that distinct roles for people of different sexes and races are supported by media that segregate the experiences of the sexes and races, while media that tend to integrate experiences for people of different races and both sexes would tend to have an egalitarian influence. In this regard, it could be argued that television, even with its often repressive content, provides a potentially liberating context. Unlike print media, which often divide people by age, sex, and level of education, television tends to include many different types of people in a similar informational sphere.

The use of new media changes "who knows what about whom" and "who knows what compared with whom." Television, in spite of its often conservative and reactionary content (and perhaps even more so because of it), has made it more difficult for us to stay in our old social places. For nothing is more frustrating than being exposed constantly to activities, adventures, and excitements that you are told are reserved for other types of people. Television has exposed women and minorities and children to parts of the culture that were once considered exclusively white adult male domains. It has also lifted many of the veils of secrecy that used to exist between the worlds of children and adults, men and women, and people of different classes, regions, and levels of education. Ironically, today's enhanced "minority consciousness" may be the result of many groups' being included informationally in the larger world and thereby coming to feel that they are physically isolated in some corner of it, restricted and disenfranchised.[9]

Unlike content and grammar, contextual analysis is generally a poor tool for political advocacy. Contextual analysis does not make traditional types of value judgments. Indeed, it offers an explanation for changes in values. Among other things, for example, the foregoing sample contextual analysis of television suggests a reason why content once considered "normal" when published in the segregating context of books has come to be seen as unacceptably sexist, racist, and discriminatory when broadcast on the integrating context of television.

MIXING METAPHORS

A number of questions about metaphors and media remain unresolved. Do the metaphors of medium as vessel/conduit, medium as language, and medium as setting/environment expose "real" aspects of media that might be difficult to see without them? Or are the aspects of media identified merely constructions of the metaphors? We should also keep in mind that the three metaphors I have discussed are actually my metaphors for others' media metaphors. Further, even if one accepts my argument that these three metaphors embrace the universe of conceptions of media to date, are there other possible conceptions?

Regardless of the answers to the above, it is clear that the separate consideration of media content, grammar, and context is an analytical fiction. The aspects of media that these metaphors highlight are not, in fact, separable. Any communication through media involves all three simultaneously.

Indeed, the three categories are not discrete but continuous. When each is pushed to its limit, it shades into the next. When the structure of content is closely studied, it blurs into grammar. A prominent face on television, for example, is implicitly a close-up; and a careful examination of the arrangement of content elements may blend easily into a study of grammatical structure. When the study of grammar is pushed to an overall analysis of the language of each medium, we start to observe what can and cannot be done with the medium regardless of manipulations of variables within it; that is, we begin to see the defining characteristics of that medium as a context.

Similarly, although content usually is downplayed in grammar and context questions, it is part of what makes such questions possible. One cannot have a low-angle shot of nothing, and a medium's context is not discernible when the medium is not used for the communication of messages. (Contextual theories of television's impact, for example, would not be very relevant to electronic snow and test patterns.)

Nevertheless, in practice, the metaphors usually operate in isolation. Although some media observers draw on more than one image, the overwhelming majority of popular and scholarly discussions of media draw primarily or exclusively on only one of these metaphors. Yet a full exploration of any topic related to media—media regulation, children and media, women and media, politics and media, and so forth—requires as broad an approach as possible. This involves considering all three images of media, either simultaneously or sequentially.

The current isolation of media images from each other has been fostered by their implicitness. Each underlying media metaphor shapes an observer's perception, molds his or her question, and predetermines half the answer—yet it is most often left unstated and unexplored. Without articulation, the latent image acts as a source of seemingly boundless vision. Once exposed, however, the limits and edges of each image begin to show, and the need to consider other images of media becomes clearer. Perhaps a more explicit confrontation with previously implicit metaphors will allow us to see new things and think new thoughts about media.

NOTES

[1] George Lakoff and Mark Johnson, *Metaphors We Live By* (Chicago: University of Chicago Press, 1980).

[2] George Renwick, *Australians and North Americans* (Yarmouth, Me.: Intercultural Press, 1980), p. 23.

[3] Jacob Bronowski, *The Origins of Knowledge and Imagination* (New Haven: Yale University Press, 1978), pp. 60–61; Robert Jay Lifton, *The Nazi Doctors: Medical Killing and the Psychology of Genocide* (New York: Basic Books, 1986). For a related exploration of how metaphors have guided psychological theory and practice, see David E. Leary, ed., *Metaphors in the History of Psychology* (New York: Cambridge University Press, 1990).

4 For an analysis of the transformation of an interview in the transcription process, see Jenny Nelson, "Phenomenology as Feminist Methodology: Explicating Interviews," in Kathryn Carter and Carole Spitzack, eds., *Doing Research on Women's Communication: Perspectives on Theory and Method* (Norwood, N.J.: Ablex, 1989), pp. 221–241.

5 Joshua Meyrowitz, "Television and Interpersonal Behavior: Codes of Perception and Response," in Gary Gumpert and Robert Cathcart, eds., *Inter/Media: Interpersonal Communication in a Media World*, 3rd ed. (New York: Oxford University Press, 1986), pp. 253–272.

6 See, for example, Sidney Aronson, "The Sociology of the Telephone," in Gumpert and Cathcart (see note 5), pp. 300–310; and Joshua Meyrowitz, *No Sense of Place: The Impact of Electronic Media on Social Behavior* (New York: Oxford University Press, 1985).

7 See, for example, Joshua Meyrowitz, "The Rise of 'Middle Region' Politics," *Et cetera*, 1977, vol. 34, pp. 133–144.

8 See, for example, Joshua Meyrowitz, "The Adultlike Child and the Childlike Adult: Socialization in an Electronic Age," *Daedalus*, 1984, vol. 113, pp. 19–48.

9 Joshua Meyrowitz, *No Sense of Place: The Impact of Electronic Media on Social Behavior* (New York: Oxford University Press, 1985). The paradoxical nature of today's minority consciousness is discussed explicitly on pages 131–135, but the arguments supporting this view are developed throughout the book.

Relative to Relativity, or It's About Time

———

JOAN RICHARDSON

All we have ever tried to do is to know our place. It's about time we got somewhere. But there is nowhere to go, nowhere to head so as to come to an end.

Relative to relativity, nothing else between 1905 and 1915 was very important. In 1905 Albert Einstein published the special theory of relativity; in 1915, the general theory. Only the later event was widely reported.

Relative to relativity, between 1905 and 1915 10 million immigrants from southern and eastern Europe entered New York City. Russia's Bloody Sunday opened 1905.

Relative to relativity, nothing since Copernicus's heliocentric theory turned the world upside down in quite the same way. Not even Newton's gravity.

Relative to relativity, it was easy to understand almost anything else. Relative to relativity, Darwin's linking us directly to a "hairy quadruped, mostly arboreal in its habits," was even more unsettling.

Everything was uncertain. People kept looking in mirrors to make sure they hadn't disappeared.

It was about time.

===

About time. Time out.

In 1905 only a few knew. They whispered about it in high-ceilinged rooms here and there. Einstein, still working in the Swiss Patent Office had published his theory in the *Annalen der Physik,* a specialized journal printed in Leipzig and read primarily by mathematicians and physicists. Max Planck and four others sat on its editorial board. Einstein also wrote in letters to some close to him of his speculations. Having come up with this revolutionary hypothesis, he began to recover a measure of equanimity. For a long time before, pondering the great uncertainties he faced, he had been experiencing nervous symptoms. For every no there was now a yes. He could sleep.

But the mind is never satisfied. And Einstein could not rest for too

long in the imperfect paradise he had imagined. There still was work
to be done.

━━

> For genuine novelty can, after all, occur in a world of blind, contin-
> gent, mechanical forces. Think of novelty as the sort of thing which
> happens when, for example, a cosmic ray scrambles the atoms in a
> DNA molecule, thus sending things off in the direction of the orchids
> or the anthropoids. The orchids, when their time came, were no less
> novel or marvelous for the sheer contingency of this necessary condi-
> tion of their existence. Analogously, for all we know, or should care,
> Aristotle's metaphorical use of *ousia,* Saint Paul's metaphorical use of
> *agape,* and Newton's metaphorical use of *gravitas,* were the results of
> cosmic rays scrambling the fine structure of some crucial neurons in
> their respective brains. Or, more plausibly, they were the results of
> some odd episodes in infancy—some obsessional kinks left in these
> brains by idiosyncratic traumata. It hardly matters how the trick was
> done. The results were marvellous. There had never been such things
> before. [1]

━━

The possibility of this thought began in 1905.

━━

Current was current. Excitement from light. It was particular. It was
new. New wave. All forms had to be reformed. New in form-a-tion for
new in-formation.

Gide's *acte gratuit,* the gratuitous act—an idea—like everything
else, something with no motive and no purpose. It is no wonder that
with this current in the air the cubists focused on structure. This, in
images.

But what about language? Ralph Waldo Emerson kept contradictions insistent. They are contradictions, however, only within a frame
that has an understood beginning, middle, and end, that seems to
progress logically along a track. But if the frame has no beginning,
middle, and end, then . . . ?

How should we write?

It's about time.

They arrived.

They arrived in hundreds of thousands, in millions.

Word groups, like quanta of light, energy, rode along new and old waves, slapping one another this way and that. Units of meaning.

New currents, connections. Space was needed, for the millions and for the new meanings. Time now had roundness and depth. No longer linear, flat. Like the discovery of a new world, a new dimension.

In the old country, as my grandmother related, my grandmother's mother's cats knew their place. They all, seven or eight of them, waited quietly and patiently, sitting in a row while the family ate. At the end of the meal they began their "neeowing" and were given their portion, the scraps that did not go to either the chickens or the goat.

Here and now my cat does not know her place—any more than any of us does. Knowing one's place is what it's all about. It's all about time. For the longest time we thought we knew, and then in 1905 Einstein began to make us twist around our old ideas, like my great-grandmother's cats around her old legs. We are still hungry for certainty. It is March 14, 1989. Einstein was born on March 14, 1879. What if he hadn't been born?

Emerson, Charles Sanders Peirce, William James, and Gertrude Stein understood. About language. "I deal forms. I shuffle and deal them out."

But we waited to hear it from Wittgenstein. Americans have always had difficulty recognizing their own authority. We wait for the news from the old world, as though the Armory Show and Derrida were the keys. We trust numbers, not words, and yet numbers lead us astray, making us believe in straight lines, triangles, and ends. We should practice counting out of sequence: music.

All we have ever tried to do is to know our place. It's about time we got somewhere. But there is nowhere to go, nowhere to head so as to come to an end.

Between 1905 and 1915 in some rooms in New York City some people were trying to get a hold of what things meant relative to relativity. Certain poets, painters, composers, and other odd sorts met here and there and played at rearranging shapes and forms, notes and rests, words and silences: Edgard Varèse, Mina Loy, Marcel Duchamp, Wallace Stevens, Francis Picabia, William Carlos Williams, Alfred Stieglitz, Mabel Dodge. . . .

===

As we take, in fact, a general view of the wonderful stream of our consciousness, what strikes us first is this different pace of its parts. Like a bird's life, it seems to be made of an alternation of flights and perchings. The rhythm of language expresses this, where every thought is expressed in a sentence, and every sentence closed by a period. The resting-places are usually occupied by sensorial imaginations of some sort, whose peculiarity is that they can be held before the mind for an indefinite time, and contemplated without changing: the places of flight are filled with thoughts of relations, static or dynamic, that for the most part obtain between the matters contemplated in the periods of comparative rest. . . .

. . . There is not a conjunction or a preposition, and hardly an adverbial phrase, syntactic form, or inflection of voice, in human speech, that does not express some shading or other of relation which we at some moment actually feel to exist between the larger objects of our thought. If we speak objectively, it is the real relations that appear revealed; if we speak subjectively, it is the stream of consciousness that matches each of them by an inward coloring of its own. In either case the relations are numberless, and no existing language is capable of doing justice to all their shades.

We ought to say a feeling of *and,* a feeling of *if,* a feeling of *but,* and a feeling of *by,* quite as readily as we say a feeling of *blue* or a feeling of *cold.* Yet we do not: so inveterate has our habit become of recognizing the existence of the substantive parts alone, that language almost refuses to lend itself to any other use. [2]

===

"And I felt and I felt and I felt as though. . . ." The children and grandchildren of the immigrants who arrived by the millions at Ellis Island often could not find the right words.

▭

Modernism not simply as an artistic movement but as the "holding in time of [our] thought"—Hegel's definition of philosophy—had its beginnings in America, where old and new, primitive and industrial, came together naturally.

▭

Sometime between 1905 and 1915 a little girl, one of the many descendants of Cornelius Vanderbilt, looked out one of the windows of the stately mansion on Fifth Avenue, somewhere in the Nineties, to see a goat munching grass before the rain. After the storm passed, the mud was thick and deep, making it hard for the goat.

At the same time, downtown along lower Broadway, in the concert saloons black musicians, recently come up from farms in the South, thumped honky-tonk pianos, playing the rhythms of their ring-shouts for white city slickers. They didn't know that their syncopations were modern, upbeat, offbeat. Muddy waters.

In a Philadelphia amusement park a little girl in a fashionable hat could not enjoy the swinging carousel ride because two swan cars behind her was a little black boy. She had no sense of the shape of things to come.

▭

Simple movement is linear, and any marked anisotropy of interaction leads under linear motion to parallel orientation. With that a cylindrical plan is born—a plan fit to encounter a streaming world with its inescapable directionality, whether of flow, of gravity or of a solid substrate.[3]

▭

Epic poets stitched together episodes in time. They rhapsodized, stitched in time.

▭

The perception of a signal happens "now," but its impulse and its transmission happened "then." In any event, the present instant is the plane upon which the signals of all being are projected. No other plane of duration gathers up universally into the same instant of becoming.[4]

It's about time.

Historical time indeed may occupy a situation near the center of the proportional scale of the possible magnitudes of time, just as man himself is a physical magnitude midway between the sun and the atom at the proportional center of the solar system, both in grams of mass and in centimeters of diameter.[5]

Celebrated events have undergone the cycle millions of times each instant throughout their history, as when the life of Jesus is commemorated in the unnumbered daily prayers of Christians. To reach us, the original event must undergo the cycle at least once, in the original event its signal, and our consequent agitation. The irreducible minimum of historical happening thus requires only an event together with its signals and a person capable of reproducing the signals.[6]

A principal aim of the historian therefore is to condense the multiplicity and the redundancy of his signals by using various schemes of classification that will spare us the tedium of reliving the sequence in all its instantaneous confusion.[7]

It's about time.

━━

Mozart was excited about opera because it is a form that allows many voices to speak at once. We should be able to place ourselves at the center of a book and have the words, ideas, spin around us. At the end of the nineteenth century Stéphane Mallarmé arranged the words and pages of his poem *Un coup de dés* like a musical score.

━━

Voices, many voices. "It's time, please. It's time," Eliot kept telling us.

Voice: Voix. Sometime between 1905 and 1915 an Alsatian with that surname arrived at Ellis Island. An error was made in transcription. His name was set down for the record as Viox. In school about sixty years later, his delicately featured granddaughter was taunted: "Vee-ox, the ox, throw rocks at Vee-ox."

> Metaphysicians tell us that unless there is some sort of common ur-vocabulary, we have no "reason" not to be cruel to those whose final vocabularies are very unlike our own.[8]

Authority. Looking at a map of the world printed onto my shower curtain, I remarked that I had always thought "Minandao" was "Mindanao." I made a mental correction of the error. A day or two later I noticed "North Carolian" in the listing of American states.

Accidentals: interpretation in music. The contingent shapes identity in this, our modern, our new world.

They held on to logic as if it were the thread leading out of the labyrinth. Flying above, Daedalus saw the intricate pattern. Abstracted by its beauty, Icarus forgot himself and his father's warning. An island formed in the cold, dark sea where he fell.

From it, in 1905, a young man set out, his pockets filled with sun-colored gold his father had given him to go to America and make his way. He came and thought that it was about time that the Brooklyn Bridge was painted.

He wrote to his father asking him to send cousins from the island. First one bridge, then another, and another. He learned well how to make his bids and whom to hire (especially prized were men with Indian blood who didn't dizzy on the towers). He prospered and grew to look like Teddy Roosevelt. He even hunted moose.

He had come to make his fortune and had. Money had its beauty. It was a kind of poetry. He forgot himself. He could not have foreseen the crash. There was no logic to it. In 1931, the hoarded gold all gone, he killed himself, another relative to relativity.

Society everywhere is in conspiracy against the manhood of every one of its members. Society is a joint-stock company, in which the members agree, for the better securing of his bread to each shareholder, to surrender the liberty and culture of the eater. . . . Nothing is at last sacred but the integrity of your own mind.[9]

So we hope some critic will show how these men's books can be put together to form a beautiful mosaic.[10]

. . .

The thought of what America,
The thought of what America,
The thought of what America would be like
    If the classics had a wide circulation
Troubles my sleep.
. . .

—Ezra Pound

NOTES

1 Richard Rorty, "The Contingency of Language," *Contingency, Irony and Solidarity* (New York: Cambridge University Press, 1989), p. 17.

2 William James, "The Stream of Thought," *Principles of Psychology*, vol. 1, pp. 224–226.

3 Philip Morison in a review of *Axis and Circumference: The Cylindrical Shape of Plants and Animals*, by Stephen A. Wainwright, in *Scientific American*, April 1989.

4 George Kubler, *The Shape of Time: Remarks on the History of Things* (New York, New Haven: Yale University Press, 1962), p. 17.

5 Ibid., p. 48, paraphrasing Harlow Shapley, *Of Stars and Men* (New York, 1958).

[6] Ibid., p. 21.

[7] Ibid., p. 23.

[8] Rorty, p. 88.

[9] Ralph Waldo Emerson, "Self-Reliance."

[10] Rorty, p. 81.

Where Linguistics, Archaeology, and Biology Meet

VITALY SHEVOROSHKIN

AND

JOHN WOODFORD

It may not be widely realized that it is just as important for us to know what words were used by humans eleven, fourteen, or even twenty thousand years ago as it is to know the genetic makeup or artifacts of these peoples. And as it is for genetics and archaeology, it is important for linguistics to determine which structures and items were not present in language at various periods in human development.

Recent discoveries of geneticists show that all present-day humans are descendants of a population that lived in Africa some one hundred thousand years ago. Luiggi Luca Cavalli-Storza and other geneticists have concluded that over the next hundreds of centuries, this population spread to other continents and that a major migration from the Near East ten thousand years ago led to the introduction of farming in Europe.

These genetic data fit the archaeological findings of Near Eastern farming and of the spread of farming peoples to Europe in the wake of earlier patterns of migration. Both the genetic and the archaeological estimates place the origin of agriculture in the Near East some three thousand years earlier than had been previously assumed.

Historical linguistics came to a similar conclusion a good deal sooner, although no one outside the field seemed to have noticed it. Linguists maintained that a language spoken in the Near East eleven thousand years ago had words for sophisticated buildings and tools, for domesticated animals, and for agricultural products. This language descended from one spoken fourteen to fifteen thousand years ago, and in that mother tongue, there were no words for domesticated plants and animals—except the word for dog, and that word could also mean wolf. Recent archaeological data show that the dog appeared some fifteen thousand years ago in the Near East, from where it traveled later to Europe and Asia.

It may not be widely realized that it is just as important for us to know what words were used by humans eleven, fourteen, or even twenty thousand years ago as it is to know the genetic makeup or artifacts of these peoples. And as it is for genetics and archaeology, it is important for linguistics to determine which structures and items were not present in language at various periods in human development.

But these observations about linguistics beg a major question: Is it possible to reconstruct languages spoken so long ago? And if so, how? The answer is, we *can* reconstruct such languages, and we can prove that the methods we use in doing so are sound and that our results are correct.

HIGH PRECISION IN THE RECONSTRUCTION OF PROTOLANGUAGES

All languages change, and all tend to "branch." If two groups of people speaking the same language lose contact, they develop different dialects. Dialects then develop into languages, which again branch into dialects, and so on. Each dialect and each language represents a well-differentiated, well-coordinated mechanism that functions according to what we can posit as rather strict rules. To discover these rules we must select stable words and forms of a given language and compare them with related words and forms of another language or languages.

Let us say that we take English words starting with the consonant *t* (*two, ten, tame, token,* and so forth). We quickly find that related words in German start with *z,* which sounds like *ts* (*zwei, zehn, zahm, zeichen*). These are stable words inherited from Proto-Germanic, the language ancestor of English and German. Non-Germanic words, cultural words—that is, words borrowed into English or German separately—will not show this correlation between initial *t* and *z.*

Adding other Germanic languages to our comparison (Yiddish, Dutch, Danish, Swedish, Flemish, Norwegian, and others) will show that the English *t-* is more stable, more archaic, than the German *z-;* that is, in the above and other stable words, English preserved the Proto-Germanic *✳t-* (the asterisk indicates that a given language or phoneme, like Proto-Germanic here, was not attested in written documents but was reconstructed by scholars; a double asterisk indicates a reconstruction from a reconstruction, and so forth), whereas in German there was a consonantal shift to *z-.*

Take another example. The English initial *th* corresponds to the German *d-,* as in *thick, thin, thing, three: dick, dünn, Ding, drei.* A comparison with other Germanic tongues again shows that German shifted the more archaic Proto-Germanic consonant *th-. As with our English t- words, here too we are dealing with stable words that mean, or denote, basic objects or concepts.

We have now established two exact phonetic correlations, English–German–Proto-German t-, z-, *t- and English–German–Proto-German th-, d-, *th-. There are many more phonetic correlations of this sort in this language family; by juxtaposing the most archaic sounds of these sister languages, we can determine the sounds of the protolanguage. This is a fundamental procedure in the reconstruction of the protolanguage. Just as we reconstructed Proto-German *t- and *th-, we can reveal correspondences for each sound of the basic words under study and thus reconstruct complete words of the protolanguage.

The mother tongue of today's Germanic languages, Proto-Germanic, was spoken around 2000 B.C.; its contemporaries included Celtic, Italic, Old Greek, and Anatolian (spoken in the region of today's Turkey).

Until the last century, it was assumed that these languages were unrelated; but the reconstruction of their ancestral language, Indo-European (IE), in 1815 showed that they were sisters, and that the ancestral tongue must have been spoken more than six thousand years ago. When Franz Bopp of Germany announced his reconstruction of IE, he did not know all of its offspring, nor did all scholars accept the IE thesis. Over the last century, however, linguists added to the IE family and increased the precision of the reconstruction of the IE protolanguage, basing their work on solid linguistic data from many languages, both dead (like Latin and Hittite) and alive. As a result of these refinements, it is generally agreed today that the IE proto-language existed and that its reconstruction reflects linguistic reality, albeit not in all details.

The reconstruction of parent languages of two families—Indo-European and Uralic (Hungarian, Finnish, Estonian, and other Finno-Ugric languages, as well as the Samoyedian languages spoken in the Soviet Union)—opened the way for the reconstruction of other protolanguages. These protolanguages include the mother tongues of such families as Afro-Asiatic (also called Semito-Hamitic—it comprises Arabic, Ethiopian, Hebrew, Berber, Cushitic, Chadic, and other languages spoken for the most part in North Africa and the Near East), Altaic (the family to which Turkic, Mongolian, Tungus, Japanese, and Korean belong), Dravidian (Malayalam, Tamil, Telugu, and other languages of southern India and Sri Lanka), and Kartvelian (Georgian and related languages of the Soviet Caucasus region).

It is generally assumed that linguistic families are unrelated. Even the few scholars who acknowledge the possibility of genetic relationship usually maintain that no one can prove such a link.

These twinned assumptions are a grave error. At one time it was assumed that different species of animals and plants were unrelated and that they did not originate from common sources. Today we know that the species are related and that humans, birds, insects, and even plants descend from a common source.

True, there have been many unsuccessful attempts to prove remote genetic relationships of "linguistic species," but these attempts were made without knowledge of the methodology of comparison and reconstruction of languages. For some reason, most such "comparatists" believed that no distinct methodology is required in this work; thus, it is understandable that many outstanding linguists became increasingly skeptical of so-called long-range comparisons.

Such comparisons have continued to be made, nonetheless, and the beginning of this century saw some remarkable results from the renowned Danish linguist Holger Pedersen. His achievements in this area are generally overlooked, but Pedersen showed that the stablest pronouns and some other basic words of Indo-European, Semitic, Uralic, and other families are not just similar but identical.

RECENT BREAKTHROUGHS IN HISTORICAL LINGUISTICS

Linguists have added some three dozen entries to Pedersen's list of words that indicate a remote relationship between different language families. Pedersen dubbed the languages so linked the Nostratic languages, from the Latin *noster* ("ours").

The most recent decisive advance in what has been called Nostratic theory was made independently in the early 1960s by two Soviet linguists, Vladislav Illich-Svitych and Aaron Dolgopolsky, who identified thousands of related words in the Nostratic languages. They established exact phonetic correspondence between these words and launched the reconstruction of the Nostratic "proto-protolanguage"—that is, the elaboration of its phonetics, grammar, and vocabulary.

According to Illich-Svitych, the Nostratic language was spoken in the Near East, perhaps in present-day Turkey, some twelve thousand years ago (Dolgopolsky's estimate is up to fifteen thousand years ago), and gradually disintegrated into several dialects that later became Nostratic daughter languages. Presumably, speakers of Afro-Asiatic (AfAs), Indo-European, and Kartvelian (Kart.) eventually settled in the West; those who spoke Uralic (Ur.), Dravidian (Drav.), and Altaic (Alt.) settled in the East. Nostratic reconstruction is based on the reconstructions of these six daughter languages (see the figure on page 180).

Scholars in the Soviet Union and Slavic countries, who had quickest access to this work, hailed it. One called it "the most important achievement in 20th century humanities," a discovery that outstripped all that linguistics had achieved in the previous decades of this century. Pioneers of distant comparisons in the West—Björn Collinder, Karl Menges, Nicolas Poppe, and others—gave very high marks to this work; a few other Western linguists, including Paul Garde of France and Americans Raimo Anttila and Henrik Birnbaum, joined them.

Soon, a few skeptical Western scholars began to accept the Nostratic reconstruction after careful investigation. A very cautious linguist, Warren Cowgill of Yale University, who was knowledgeable in both Indo-European and Uralic languages, said a decade ago that he accepted the theory, but he added that it would be another forty years before it became "common knowledge." Others remained skeptical.

Dolgopolsky, who moved to Israel in 1977, says Western scholars'

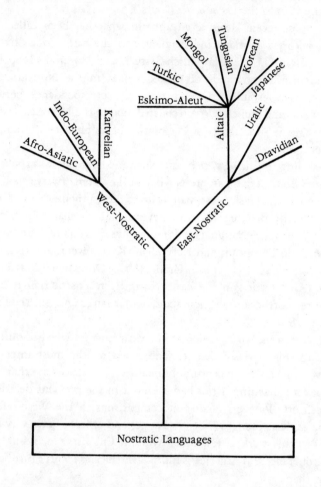

resistance to Nostratic theory stems from two facts: First, the dictionary of Nostratic, which Illich-Svitych began, is available only in Russian. (Three volumes have been published—in 1971, 1976, and 1984—and work on the project continues.) Second, the vast majority of linguists specialize in rather narrow fields—the Semitologists sticking to Semitic languages, the Turkologists to Turkic, and so forth, while paying no attention to neighboring linguistic fields—

and remain indifferent, if not hostile, to attempts to connect "their" languages with any that are "alien" to them. Nevertheless, despite the lack of acceptance in some influential corners of the linguistic world, Dolgopolsky continues to contribute greatly to the dictionary.

Illich-Svitych, who was only thirty-one when he died in 1966, had completed only the first part of his dictionary, but his note cards contain data that are essential for the editors who are carrying on his work. The three published books contain 378 entries, each covering one Nostratic root. This represents more than half of all roots Illich-Svitych reconstructed. (The first and third volumes are in some Western libraries; the 1976 work was published privately and is still unavailable in the West.)

At an international conference on language and biology held in Turin, Italy, in May 1988, Dolgopolsky told participants that Illich-Svitych owed his success to his knowledge of scores of languages, his "phenomenal memory," and his ability to discover and prove the relatedness of seemingly unrelated, or at best loosely related, facts.

The Nostratic dictionary and Illich-Svitych's notes for future volumes contain hundreds of terse comments that have proved very fruitful for linguists who specialize in semantics, typology of languages, phonetics, morphology, and syntax, or in such fields as Indo-European, Afro-Asiatic, Dravidian, Turkic, and Uralic. (Indo-Europeanists, who are now somewhat at sea because IE languages lack sufficient data for the unequivocal reconstruction of IE consonants, vowels, and laryngeals [*h*-type sounds], should consult Nostratic; being based on many languages, Nostratic is more reliable and precise in this respect and explains the *origin* of IE sounds, grammatical elements, and words.)

SOME FIFTEEN-THOUSAND-YEAR-OLD WORDS

The most stable words in any language are pronouns of the first and second person (I and me; thou, thee, and you). Indeed, Nostratic languages show remarkable similarity in these pronouns.

According to the reconstructions, the Nostratic daughter languages had the following first-person forms: IE *me, Kartv. *me and *mi, Ur. *mi, and similar forms in the other three languages. Verbal endings conformed with such first-person endings as IE *-mi, AfAs *-mi, and so on. From this evidence, we can reconstruct the Nostratic pronoun **mi for "I" (the double asterisk, we remind the reader, indicates that the reconstruction is itself based upon a reconstruction).

According to the rules of Nostratic sounds, the vowel i could become e in Western languages; this explains the *me of IE and Kartv. from the Nostratic **mi. The form of the dative and accusative cases is **mi-nV ("to me," "me"), with a suffix (V stands for an unclear vowel); it is reconstructed on the following data: IE *me-ne, Kartv. *me-n-, Ur. and Alt. *mi-nV, and similar forms.

In the second-person verbal forms, we have, for instance, the IE verbal ending *-si for "thou"; Kartv. *se-, *si- for "thee"; Alt. *si- for "thou"; and so on. The Nostratic reconstruction is **si for "thou." Turkic/Altaic *se-n- shows that the dative and accusative case ("to thee", "thee") of this Nostratic pronoun was apparently **si-nV, a parallel to the first pronoun *mi-nV, "me."

Other Nostratic pronouns included two forms of the first-person plural "we"—inclusive (that is, "we and you") and exclusive ("we without you"); this precise differentiation was apparently significant for our remote ancestors, but only a few daughter languages have preserved traces of this distinction. Such a distinction as "our" people as opposed to "your" people was very important for ancient peoples, who lived in tribes and cared about being different from other tribes. The social manifestation of this separateness is observed in the requirement that men of one tribe marry women of a different tribe. Australian and southern African tribes still preserve both the linguistic forms and the marital taboos.

Full words in Nostratic could have one of two shapes: either consonant-vowel-consonant-vowel or consonant-vowel-consonant-consonant-vowel. An examination of the reconstruction of a few words beginning with initial glottal (throaty) t will show the sound correspondences between Nostratic (Nostr.) and its daughter languages.

(Glottal *t* is symbolized by *T* and can be felt if one pronounces the *ts* in *button* or *cotton*.)

1. Nostr. **TarV*, "to rub"; AfAs *TVr-*, "to whet, sharpen" (as in the Arabic root *Trr*); IE *ter-*, "rub"; Drav. *tar-*, "rub, break off"; Alt. *TarV*, "to scratch" (as in Turkish *tara-*). The vowel *a* is reconstructed from Asian East Nostratic languages, which have well-preserved Nostratic vowels.

2. Nostr. **TumV*, "dark"; AfAs *Tum*, "dark"; Ur. *tumV*, "dark"; IE *tem-*, "dark." (Different Nostr. vowels merged into *e* in IE; in this case Nostr. **u* became IE *e*.)

By comparing many words beginning with *T* and *t*, Illich-Svitych established this phonetic correspondence: Nostr. **T* evolved to AfAs *T*, IE *t*, Ur. and Drav. *t*, and Alt. *T*.

Nostratic also had words that began with **t*. Here are the phonetic correspondences of Nostratic and its daughter languages for the adjectives *long* and *proper*:

Nostr. **telḥV*, "long" (the *ḥ* as in English *heavy*); AfAs *tVlḥ-* (as in Arabic root *tlḥ*, "be long"); IE *delḥ-*, "long"; Alt. *telV*, "long, broad" (Nostr. **ḥ* disappears in Alt.).

Nostr. **taKe* or **take* (*K* is a glottal *k*), "suitable, proper"; AfAs *tk-n-*, "put into order"; IE *dek-*, "suitable, proper" (a frontal *k* as in English *keen*); Drav. *takkV*, *takV*, "be suitable, to fit." Dravidian *a* originates from either Nostr. **a-* or **ä-*. (An umlaut indicates that the vowel is pronounced toward the front of the mouth, as *u* in French *déjà vu*.)

We find the following correspondence: Nostr. **t* becomes AfAs *t*, IE *d*, Drav. and Ur. *t*, and Alt. *t*. This is an exact correlation. In Kartvelian we always find the same consonants as in AfAs: *T* from Nostr. **T*, *t* from **t*, and so on. Recent discoveries show that IE originally also had initial *T* and *t*, as in AfAs, and Kartv., but that in most IE daughter languages, these initial consonants changed to *t* and *d*, respectively. In table 1 on page 184,

TABLE 1: SOME ENGLISH WORDS OF NOSTRATIC ORIGIN[1]

Nostratic[2]	Indo-European[3]	English
**bari "take"	*bher- "take, bring, carry"	bring
**boŕa "brown"	*bher-, *bhreu- "brown"	brown
**bulV "mix," etc.	*bhl-endh- "mix"	blend
**bura "to bore"	*bher- "to bore"	bore
**buŕa "to boil, seethe"	*bhreu- "boil, seethe"	brew
**bVlHV "blow"	*bhelH- "blow"	blow
**bVnTV "tie together"	*bhendh- "tie together"	bind
**HosV "ash-tree"	*Hos- "ash-tree"	*ash*-tree
**HuKa "eye, see"	*Hokʷ- "eye, see"	eye
**ʔitä "eat"	*Hed- "eat"	eat
**karV, **kurV "crane" (bird)	*ger-H- "crane"	crane
**käjwV "chew"	*gieu- "chew"	chew
**kENHV "know"	*ǵenH-/*ǵneH- "know"	know
*küjñA "bend, joint"	*ǵenu/*ǵneu "knee"	knee
**küni "woman"	*gʷen- "woman, wife"	queen
**KaPV "head"	*kap-ut- "head"	head
**KerdV "chest, heart"	*kerd- "heart"	heart
**KVrpV "gather fruits"	*kerp- "gather fruits"	harvest
**KaLi "arise"	*kel-H- "arise; hill"	hill
**KäPä "paw"	*kep-H- "hoof, paw"	hoof
**KErV "horn"	*ker- "horn"	horn
**KirV "hoar-frost"	*ker- "hoar-frost"	*hoar*-frost
**Ko "who"	*kʷo- "who"	who
**KorV "gnaw, worm"	*kʷr-mi- "worm"	worm
**KüjnA "wolf, dog"	*kuōn, kun- "wolf," "dog"	hound
**KUpa "heap"	*keup/b- "heap"	heap

Notes:
[1] The list is based on the first volume of Illich-Svitych's Nostratic dictionary (published in Moscow in 1971).

[2] Nostratic was spoken in the Near East some fourteen or fifteen thousand years ago. *Nostr.* V = some vowel; ŕ = soft r; H = a kind of h; N = a kind of n; L = a kind of l; A = ä or a; U = u; E = ä, e, or i; K, P, T = glottal k, p, t; j = y.

[3] Indo-European was spoken in Anatolia some six thousand or more years ago. *Indo-Europ.* bh, dh = aspirated b, d; H = a kind of k; ǵ = soft k, g; kʷ = "rounded" k (as in *queen*); gʷ = "rounded" g; ō = long o.

Nostratic words are given that begin with *b, *k, *K, and other consonants. English "offspring" of these words are also provided.

Including the two pronouns, we have now looked at six roots, or words, which represent less than 1 percent of the items reconstructed by Illich-Svitych. The few linguists who have closely studied these reconstructions agree that the correspondences *cannot be explained by chance*: these words belong together.

Does that mean that these linguists also accept Nostratic theory? No, it does not.

Some linguists say, "The fact that these words are related does not mean that the languages they are part of are related. These correspondences are evidence of borrowings from one language into another." This argument ignores the important fact that Illich-Svitych chose words that are not subject to borrowing.

Anti-Nostraticists explain the correspondence between Uralic *wete, "water," and IE *wed-, "water" (as in Hittite *watar.* English *water, wet,* and so forth), by saying that Uralic speakers must have borrowed the word. The Nostraticists contend, however, that this correspondence can be explained only by assuming that Ur. and IE preserved the word for water from a common ancestor, which they reconstruct as Nostr. **wete. Can it be argued reasonably that speakers of Uralic did not know water, or had no name for it, before they encountered Indo-Europeans?

And the Nostraticists have another powerful argument: Nostr. **wete has survived not only in Uralic, but also in Drav. *wetV and *ōtV-, "wet" (ō sounds like the vowel in the English *straw*) and in Tungus (Altaic) *ödV-, "rain." Here also, phonetic changes from Nostr. to respective daughter languages follow exact rules: Nostr. *t* between vowels becomes IE and Alt. *d*, and Ur. and Drav. *t*.

The Nostr. reconstruction of the word for chest is **Kerd-, which gave rise to Kartv. *m-Kerd, "chest"; IE *kerd-, "heart"; and English "heart." Critics argue that the Kartvelians must have borrowed the word from IE, but in doing so they ignore the fact that linguists have reconstructed the Afro-Asiatic word as *KVrd-. This word is present only in southern AfAs languages, which have never been in contact with IE or Kartv. This means we have a common word inherited from the Nostr. mother tongue and preserved in at least three daughter languages: AfAs, IE, and Kartv.

Many other stable words common to Kartv. and IE are said to have entered Kartv. through borrowings from IE, including words for blood, jaw, and warm. It defies what we know of linguistic development to propose that Kartvelians did not know what blood or jaws were and had no concept of warmth. The evidence does indicate, however, that more than eight thousand years ago in eastern Anatolia there was a common Indo-European–Kartvelian language, a descendant of Nostratic, that later split into IE and Kartv. Around that time, the Kartvelians began to move to the southern Caucasus.

The Indo-Europeans lived in Anatolia until around six thousand years ago, when some tribes began migrating to the Balkan region and became the West Europeans. Thus, for example, the IE word *ekwos,* "horse," is found only in West-IE languages. The Hittite-Luvian branch of the IE family remained in Anatolia.

Similarly, the data show that another common ancestral language of the IE-Kartv. type was Uralo-Dravidian. It was spoken some eight thousand years ago in central Asia and later split into Uralic, whose speakers moved northwest to the Ural region, and Dravidian, whose speakers moved southward until they arrived in northern India. By the time Dravidian reached southern India, it had split into several daughter languages.

In some cases, of course, a Uralic or Kartv. word was borrowed from IE, and as Illich-Svitych showed, there are IE words borrowed from Semitic. But in such cases, these are *cultural words,* not basic words.

Basic words—those that resist substitution by borrowing—include pronouns, body parts, natural terms (sun, moon, fire, night, day, water, sea, rock, dirt), terms for people (man, woman, boy, girl), basic verbs (die, walk, see, hear, burn, eat, cook), basic qualities (hot, cold, big, plenty, hungry, thirsty, dark, bright), and so forth.

Cultural words included terms for sacrifice, master, buy, sell, lock, key, to plow, the number seven *(septm),* sophisticated tools, domesticated plants, and animals. The American scholars Bomhard, Levin, and Brown maintain that the IE and Semitic words for bull—*tauros and *caur-, respectively—were inherited from a common parent language. But this is a cultural word designating a domestic animal, and its sound correspondences are not typical for Nostratic words inherited by both IE and AfAs.

Illich-Svitych showed in 1964 that Indo-Europeans borrowed their word for bull from Semites some six thousand years ago. The Semites' culture was more developed than the Indo-Europeans', and the latter borrowed elements of the former's culture, in addition to several dozen words. Other IE borrowings from AfAs include *nau-, "ship," from *nVw-; *peleku, "axe," from *pVlVk; *septm, "seven," from *shVbatum; *ario-, "master," from *HVr-, "freeborn,"; *ghaid-, "goat," from *gadju; *dhwer-, "door/fence," from *Tur-, "fence/yard."

It should be reemphasized that the crucial argument for remote genetic relationship rests upon the commonality of first and second person pronouns, as well as a fair number of very stable words that simply cannot have been borrowed and therefore are the strongest evidence of the existence of the Nostratic proto-protolanguage.

The reliability of Nostratic reconstruction is demonstrated by very exact rules that cover relations between every sound of a given word in a given language and corresponding sounds in related words in all other Nostratic languages (see table 1 on page 184).

THE MOST RECENT DISCOVERIES

Although Illich-Svitych died and Dolgopolsky left the Soviet Union, their pupils in Moscow and Leningrad continue to study the remote relationship of languages. Two of the most talented of these comparatists are Sergei Starostin and Sergei Nikolaev, who have reconstructed Sino-Dene Caucasian, a macrofamily, or phylum, of languages as ancient as Nostratic.

Sino-Dene-Caucasian was spoken by people living to the northeast of the Nostrates, perhaps in the Ural Mountains region; it is the ancestor of four daughter languages—North Caucasian (proto-language of modern Adyghan, Abkhazian, and Daghestanian), Sino-Tibetan (protolanguage of Chinese, Burmese, and Tibetan), Yeniseian (spoken in western Siberia near the Arctic Circle), and Na-Dene, or Athapascan (the Eyak-Athapascan languages are spoken today by Native Americans).

Several "mystery languages," whose ancestry has long baffled scholars, have been traced to the North Caucasian branch of Sino-Caucasian, including Basque (spoken in areas of Spain and France), Hurri-Urartian (a dead language once spoken south of the Caucasus Mountains; the name of the Armenian's sacred Mount Ararat bears the same root as Urartu, a kingdom located near present-day eastern Turkey), and Hatti (a language spoken four thousand years ago in Anatolia; its name survived in "Hittite," the name of an ancient people who invaded and settled in the Hatti region). Furthermore, it appears that Etruscan (the language of pre-Roman Italy) and Bur-ushaski (a language spoken in northern Pakistan even today) belong to the North Caucasian branch of the Sino-Caucasian languages.

A third phylum of languages has been classified by two American linguists at Stanford University, Joseph Greenberg and Merritt Ruhlen. Greenberg calls this the Amerind phylum; it contains most American Indian languages except the Athapascan (Navaho, Apache, and other Na-Dene languages, which belong to the Dene-Caucasian phylum) and Eskimo-Aleutian (which seem to be Altaic and therefore Nostratic).

Four other phyla have been identified, although the taxonomic work on them is still incomplete. They are as follows:

1. Austric languages, which include Austronesian (Indonesian, Bali, Malay, Javanese, and Malagasy, along with the Melanesian, Micro-nesian, and Polynesian families), Tai, and the Austro-Asiatic lan-guages (Vietnamese, Muong, Khmer, and other languages of Southeast Asia)

2. Australian and Indo-Pacific languages

3. Niger-Nilotic, or Congo-Saharan, languages, represented by two

African families—the Niger-Kordofanian (Fulani, Swahili, Ashanti, Yoruba, Bantu, and other languages spoken primarily in south central and western Africa) and Nilo-Saharan (spoken in central Africa and regions of the Sahara, Mali, Lake Chad, Tanzania, Zaire, and elsewhere south of the Sahara)

4. Khoisan languages, probably the most ancient family, including the southern African languages Hottentot and Bushman, which employ the clicking sounds that may originate from several consonants used in the earliest human speech

These seven phyla cover almost all languages of the world. (See the figure on page 190.)

When the classification has been completed, each language of the world, dead or alive, should find a place in its proper phylum. In the meantime, however, it has become more and more clear to linguists who are making remote comparisons that *all of the world's languages are genetically related,* that they originated from some ancient mother tongue—the "Proto-World" language. This is surely a more reasonable conclusion than that they are unrelated.

Still, many questions remain to be settled. When was this first world language spoken? How has it evolved? What principles should govern the classification of proto-protolanguages? Greenberg thinks that Nostratic, which he calls Eur-Asiatic, is closer to Amerind than to the other macrofamily parents. And indeed, the similarities between Nostratic and Amerind vocabularies are striking.

Other scholars, however, maintain that the closest relative of the Amerind branch is the Austric, since both share many of the stablest word forms, including the personal pronouns **ni and **mi for "I" and "thou," respectively.

In any event, by comparing Nostratic, Amerind, Dene-Caucasian, and the other most ancient sister languages, we may reconstruct some earlier intermediary protolanguage, if not the original mother tongue, and thus learn something about what life was like in those remote times. When reconstructing Proto-World, linguists should try to reveal the *exact* sound correspondences and refrain from playing with

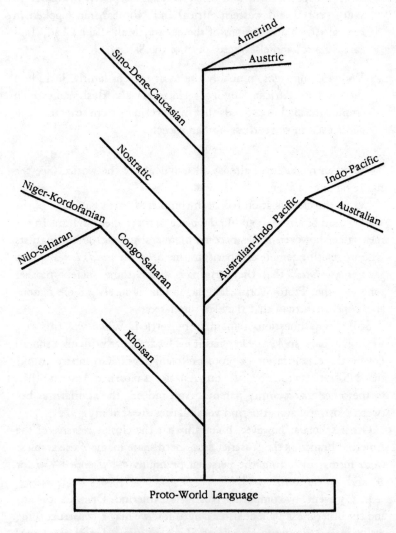

Seven Phyla of World Languages

similarities, as some did in the twenties and fifties. See table 2 on pages 192 and 193, where some Proto-World words are cited, along-side their "offspring" in different languages, including English.

COLLABORATION OF LINGUISTS
AND ARCHAEOLOGISTS

The birth of a dialect, or "separate language," is a process involving the disintegration of the parent tongue. Since Indo-European evolved from Nostratic in the course of over seven thousand years or so—perhaps beginning as far back as 15,000 to 14,000 B.C.—we should expect to find the development of human society reflected in linguistic changes. Naturally, when speaking about a society that old, one should envisage it as using Nostratic words, not Indo-European, not Egyptian or Semitic, not even Hittite.

Reconstructed words show us that IE was a language of a rather highly developed urban society, although not as developed as the contemporaneous Semitic society. Nostratic, on the other hand, was a language of hunters and gatherers. This conclusion is indicated not only by the age of Nostratic, but also by its vocabulary. Speakers of Nostratic had no words for domesticated animals and plants; during their time there was no animal husbandry, no farming. The only word presaging humankind's economic development back then was **KüjnA, which meant both "wolf" (as in Uralic *küjnä) and "dog" (as in IE *kuōn, which gave rise to such forms as Latin *canis* and English *hound*). Celtic languages, by the way, testify that IE *kuōn also meant wolf, so here the archaic meaning is preserved as well.

A few Nostratic words, however, indicate rather sophisticated techniques of producing pottery, building shelters, and erecting fences. Nostratic **KadV, for example, originally meant plait/ wattle, which was the technique used for making fences, buildings, and pots. This word became the AfAs *KVd-, "build, make pots"; the Kartv. *Ked, "build"; IE *kedh-/ket-, "build, room, pot"; Drav. *kattu, "build," "to bundle," "a sack" (*tt* indicates a retroflexive

TABLE 2: SOME ENGLISH WORDS OF "PROTO-WORLD" ORIGIN

English[1]	Indo-Eur.	Nostr.	Proto-World	Amerind	Sino-Dene-Caucas.	Other Lang.[2]
be	bheuə-	buHi	buHi "be, stay"	bubi		
(aqua-)	Hak''-	HaKu	HaKu "water"	Hakw-	Ku, k''a	Au kVuV, IP kw
eat	Hed-	itä	Hitä "eat"	HitV		
eye	Hok''-	HuKa	HuKa "eye, see"	HuKV		Kh, NN HVkuV, Au Hu
queen	g''en-, ke, ko	kiimi	kumi "woman"	kuni	kUn-kV	NN, As kumi, Au kVn
be		Ki	Ki "this"	Ki, Ko		
born	ker	KErV	KErV "horn"	KirV		
bound	kuon, kun-	KüijnA	Kujan "wolf"	Kujan "dog"	kbujVn	Kh Kwin, Au kun "dog"
who	k''e-, k''i-	Ko	Ka(n)[3] "who"	Ka(n), Ko	ku(n)	Kh Ka(n), NN kV
scent, smart	sen-, sme(u)	L/San(g)V	Lun(g)V "smell, nose"	L/SunV	SVn(g)V	Kh C/Sun- "nose", As Con-
(manu-) "hand"	maH-n- "take, hand"	maHV	maHV "take"	maH-n- "hand"		Au ma-maRa "take, hand"
(magn-), more	meg(b)-	magV	magV "big, large"	mag/kV		
(ameliorate, multi)	mel-	malV	malV "plenty"	malin "good"		
man	manu, onu	manV	manV "man, male"	mano "husband"	mVnXV "man, male"	As manu "man, male," Au man- "man"
(remain, permanent)	men-	mänV	mänV "stay"	manV, EnV	mEn-	IP man-, mEn- "sit"

mean, mind	*men-*	*manu*	*mänV* "think, wish"	*mena*	*mVn-*	NN *malim-* "think, know"
many	*men(gb)-*	*mon(g)V*	*mon(g)V* "many"	*moni*		
us	*ne-ʃ* "us"	*naH* "we" (exclus.)	*naH* "we"	*naH* "we"		Au *ni-* "sit"
nest	*ni-zdo* "nest" / *niH-* "down" + *sed-* "sit"	*niH-*	*niHV* "down"	*ni-* "sit"		
nose	*neus-*	*niL/Su*	*niL/Su*	*niL/SV*		
nose	*nas-*	*naS-*	*naS-* "nose"	*naS-*		
tongue	*dngbu*	*Nina, NangV*	*NigV*	*Nig-, Neme, NangV,* "tongue"	*Nangi*	
fire	*paxw-r*	*PiuV*	*PiuV* "fire"	*Pixw-*	*ʔP(i)Hu*	
(senile)	*sen-* "old, year"	*SVnV*	*Si/anV* "old"	*Sulim-*	*Sin-* "old"	
that	*to*	*Tä*	*Tä* "that"	*Ta* "that", *tV* "that, this"		

Notes:

[1] English words in parentheses are borrowings from Latin.

[2] The languages in this column are abbreviated as follows: As = Austric (Austronesian, Tai, or Austro-Asiatic); Au = Australian; IP = Indo-Pacific; Kh = Khosian; NN = Niger-Nilotic (Niger-Kordofanian or Nilo-Saharan).

[3] Letters in parentheses indicate variants. For example, *Ku(n)* means *Kun* or *ku*.

pronunciation, in which the tip of the tongue curves backward, like the *t* sound in *butter* or *water*).

The linguistic evidence conforms with archaeological findings. A few years ago, Soviet linguist Alexander Militarev joined in the reconstruction of a proto–Afro-Asiatic language that may have been spoken some eleven thousand years ago. He contacted an archaeologist, Victor Shnirel'man (author of *Origin of Cattle-Breeding*), who was working on the most ancient civilizations of the Near East. They compared their data and concluded that the linguist's words from proto–Afro-Asiatic that designate objects and processes typical for the Afro-Asiatic lifestyle thoroughly fit archaeological evidence as provided by the Natufian culture, which was located on the territory of Palestine and Syria and appears to have been a contemporary of speakers of proto-AfAs.

The points of linguistic-archaeological matching cover southern animals (including the lion), landscape features (both desert and groves—even rivers), plant life (olives, figs), and the architecture of dwellings (roundish and built from twigs with a stone upper part, a door, a wall between two rooms, and a raised section). The landscape terms indicate a territory on the border of a desert and forest zone with typical Mediterranean trees, bushes, and other flora.

Reconstructed words from proto-AfAs fit the archaeological findings of tools; pots, pumpkin bottles, and other vessels; plates; mats; knives; arrows; arrowheads; and wooden objects used by the Natufians. Specific words existed for different construction techniques, as well as for paint and paintings. The vocabulary clearly indicates that reeds were used to build various objects. The people worked with clay (several words describe clay pots) but in the main used stone, wooden, and leather vessels. Handmade objects were plaited or woven, including cloth and baskets.

These correspondences also extended to types of food, including barley and wheat flour; processes of meal preparation; such techniques as sowing, plowing, and furrowing; and certain fruits, trees, birds, and domesticated animals, including the dog, goat, and sheep. A number of words indicate that these people continued to hunt and gather *(bow, arrow, animal trap, dart)* and to rely for the most part on stone and bone tools, as they had long before.

The results of these comparative studies, furthermore, agree fully with the chronology established by radiocarbon dating and other analyses. Shnirel'man is now reconstructing the ways of life of certain ancient peoples of Southeast Asia. He has elaborated some standard procedures of linguistic-archaeological reconstructions in a theoretical monograph on the subject.

In his recent and much discussed book *Archaeology and Language: The Puzzle of Indo-Europeans* (Cambridge, 1987), British archaeologist Colin Renfrew maintains that the people who inhabited southern Anatolia (the southeastern area of modern Turkey) nine to ten thousand years ago were Indo-Europeans. He says they knew agriculture and carried knowledge of it to Greece and then to eastern Europe during migrations between six thousand and seventy-two hundred years ago. They also domesticated the horse and introduced it to other societies during migrations from eastern Europe. Renfrew notes that his view corresponds with the findings of Cavalli-Storza and other geneticists.

This hypothesis squares with the linguistic evidence presented by the "Nostratic school." The Nostraticists base their thesis on the many cultural words that the Indo-Europeans borrowed into their language eight thousand or so years ago from their more advanced neighbors to the south—the Semites. Among these words were many agricultural terms: apparently, agriculture came to the Indo-Europeans from the Semites.

Renfrew agrees, too, that the Semitic languages (part of the Hamito-Semitic, or Afro-Asiatic, branch of Nostratic languages) originated to the south of Anatolia, but it seems difficult, he adds, "to hazard a guess about the language of the Natufians of Palestine," who are among the first Semitic peoples we know about. As we have mentioned, it was in the Natufian region that the Afro-Asians—the ancestors of the Semites—developed agriculture over eleven thousand years ago.

Renfrew seems not to know of Nostratic theory and thus does not know how linguistic evidence explains the arrival of Indo-Europeans in Anatolia. But like the Nostraticists, he places this event at about nine thousand years ago—four to five thousand years earlier than the widely held estimates.

Because of his unfamiliarity with Nostratic theory, Renfrew wants to place the origin of the Indo-European culture as far back as forty thousand years ago. Knowledge of the linguistic evidence should convince him that the direct ancestors of the Indo-Europeans were people whose descendants became both Indo-European and Kartvelian. The parent language of both Indo-European and Kartvelian was spoken in the Near East eleven thousand or more years ago. These Indo-European/Kartvelians, alongside the Afro-Asian, Uralo-Dravidian, and Altaic peoples, originated from a Near Eastern tribe that, for want of better name, we must now call the Nostrates—but even they lived only fourteen thousand years ago, not forty thousand. Still, linguists can go beyond Nostratic and reconstruct "Proto-World," of which Nostratic was a daughter (see tables 1 and 2 on pages 184 and 192–193).

ON THE COLLABORATION OF LINGUISTS AND GENETICISTS

Many more geneticists than archaeologists have been quick to recognize that historical linguistics can offer valuable information in their attempts to penetrate as deeply as possible into human prehistory. They have shown that the spread of population groups, as traced by genetic biology, coincided with the spread of languages, as shown by remote linguistic comparison and reconstruction.

At the Turin conference, Cavalli-Storza showed that the earliest human migrations, which started with the split of Khoisan-speaking groups in southern Africa, essentially coincide with the spread of respective proto-protolanguages. This would appear to support the identification of major linguistic phyla and the reconstruction of their respective mother tongues (see the figure on page 190).

Several critics have argued that reconstruction of Nostratic or even older languages is unsound because it ignores the fact that the putative Nostratic and other proto-protocommunities comprised many dispersed villages, and thus that humankind's earliest language would have atomized into dialects or different languages rather quickly, giving rise to languages that were unrelated or whose relationship could not be proved.

The geneticists, however, showed that strong family and kinship traditions and very low population densities kept the pattern of genetic structures and their geographic distribution regular enough to be traced and identified today, tens of thousands of years later.

It is altogether likely, therefore, that the development and spread of languages correlate with genetic patterns, and that population "grouplets" living over a wide area could well have spoken languages or dialects that originated from a given protolanguage and then spread in certain directions among certain population groups, just as the genetic material was distributed.

It is significant that the chronology provided by genetics shows a much older age than the less precise linguistic chronology. Linguists, it seems, have sharply underestimated the age of the most ancient languages, including the hypothetical Proto-World language. Progress in linguistic reconstruction and in glottochronology (dating of protolanguages) may soon provide linguists with figures that correspond more closely to genetic chronology.

To bring even more light and clarity of focus to humanity's remote past, what is now needed is better-organized and more intense cooperation among archaeologists, physical and cultural anthropologists, mythologists, geneticists, mathematicians, computer specialists, and linguists.

The School of the Future

HOWARD GARDNER

American education is at a turning point. There are considerable pressures to move very sharply in one direction, a direction I will call "uniform schooling"; there is also the possibility that our educational system can strike off in a fresh direction, which I term "individual-centered schooling." A struggle is under way at this moment about the probable direction in which the schools will veer. My own analysis of the scientific evidence indicates that we should as a polity move in the direction of individual-centered schooling.

As if it were the weather, everyone is talking these days about the desperate need for educational reform in the United States. The reasons for this heightened concern are not difficult to identify. To begin with, there is the perceived economic challenge from Japan and other Pacific Rim countries; no longer is the United States the undisputed industrial and scientific leader of the world. Added to this is the clear decline in literacy and common cultural knowledge documented by a number of statistical indices, official white papers, and the best-selling works of Allan Bloom and E. D. Hirsch. Finally, there is Americans' virtual compulsion to reexamine the quality and mission of their schools at least once each generation. These and other pressures combine to make the current concern about education nearly inevitable. And yet, again like the weather, there is the considerable chance that the talk will remain mere talk, that each interested party will look to others to institute reform, and that, in the end, changes wrought in the educational system will be modest.

As I see it, American education is at a turning point. There are considerable pressures to move very sharply in one direction, a direction I will call "uniform schooling"; there is also the possibility that our educational system can strike off in a fresh direction, which I term "individual-centered schooling." A struggle is under way at this moment about the probable direction in which the schools will veer. My own analysis of the scientific evidence indicates that we should as a polity move in the direction of individual-centered schooling. In what follows, I indicate why and how such an education might be achieved.

———

At present the most vocal contributors to the debate are calling for uniform schools. Stripped to its essentials, their argument goes as follows. There is a basic set of competences, and a core body of knowledge, that every individual in our society should master. Some individuals are more able than others and can be expected to master this knowledge more rapidly. Schools should be set up in such a way as to ensure that the most gifted can move to the top and that the greatest number of individuals will achieve basic knowledge as efficiently as possible. For that reason, there should be the same curriculum for all students, the same methods of teaching, and the same "standardized" methods of assessment. Students, teachers, administrators, school districts, states, and even the whole nation should be judged in terms of the efficiency and effectiveness with which these common standards are achieved. Paying attention to individual differences is at best a luxury, at worst a dangerous deviation from essential educational priorities.

Of course, it is an oversimplification to band together under one slogan the whole gamut of critics of education in America today. There are clear differences among E. D. Hirsch, Allan Bloom, Mortimer Adler, William Bennett, and the representatives of municipal, state, and federal agencies, not to mention such private-interest groups as the Heritage Foundation and the Twentieth Century Fund. What unites them, and justifies their being grouped beneath one ample neoconservative umbrella, is their dissatisfaction with "progressive" ideas in American education, their hunger for a capacious store of common knowledge and skills, and their impatience with approaches that cherish the individuality of each student, teacher, and school building.

It would be wrong to dispute every paragraph of the neoconservative critique—and, in any case, it is unnecessary. Along with many others who are dissatisfied with the uniform view, I certainly believe that the literacy of American students ought to be improved, that every student ought to have the opportunity to master certain basic disciplines, and that much of the educational program of the 1960s (and of earlier decades) was not well considered. Yet I am equally convinced that many of the cures suggested by the neoconservative reformers are worse than the disease, and that the proposed cures will not heal the patients.

My fundamental quarrel with the uniform view comes from my

conviction that it is grounded in a basically flawed view of human cognition—what I have called "IQ-style thinking." As is well known the first intelligence tests were designed nearly a century ago with the reasonable goal of predicting which students were likely to encounter difficulties with standard school curricula. Over the years, psychologists have in fact been able to identify a set of short-answer items that predicts school performance with some success.

In the last eighty or so years, however, this line of thinking has grown completely out of keeping with its legitimate scope. Where once a single instrument was used for a circumscribed purpose, now hundreds of paper-and-pencil standardized tests are used for a variety of purposes, from recommendations for "special education" to college admission to "wall-chart" comparisons among nations. Where once these tests were introduced as supplements to an ongoing curriculum, now schools and programs are specially designed to improve performance on these instruments, with little attention to the meaning of such improvements. It is not an exaggeration to say that we have let the testing tail wag the curricular dog. Nor is it an exaggeration to say that the IQ test has led the way inexorably to the current intoxication with the uniform school.

Paradoxically, at the very time when IQ-style thinking has made unprecedented inroads into thinking about educational programs, the slender scientific base on which it was erected has almost completely crumbled. From a number of disciplines interested in human cognition has come strong evidence that the mind is a multifaceted, multicomponent instrument, which cannot in any legitimate way be captured in a single paper-and-pencil–style instrument.[1] As this point of view gains in plausibility, the need to rethink educational goals and methods becomes profound.

The evidence challenging IQ-style thinking has come from the range of academic disciplines that probe the human mind.[2] Neurobiologists have documented that the human nervous system is highly differentiated. Quite specific neural centers process different kinds of "information"; for example, language capacities are mediated by certain zones in the left hemisphere, while spatial and musical functions are served primarily by regions in the right hemisphere. Any thought that the brain is a single-purpose or infinitely "plastic" organ has been fully discredited.

Proceeding quite independently, research in artificial intelligence has moved steadily away from uniformist thinking. Two decades ago, computer scientists quested for general problem-solving mechanisms that could deal with the full range of intellectual domains, from scientific discovery to chess. However, recent advances have occurred almost entirely through the development of "expert systems" that contain highly detailed knowledge about specific domains (such as medical diagnosis) and exhibit little or no "transfer" to other domains.

And what of my own discipline of psychology? A generation ago, most psychologists believed in general laws of learning, perception, memory, and attention that are applicable across diverse contents; what was true of the college sophomore would be true for the Norwegian rat and for all species in between. Behavioristically oriented psychologists believed as well that the human mind could be adapted to deal with any kind of information in an equally skilled way. But with every year, further evidence accumulates showing deep constraints in the human mind. Certain patterns of growth are easy to achieve, while others are elusive; the basic cognitive processes at work in one area (say, language) are quite distinct from those at work in other areas (such as spatial cognition or social understanding).

In an effort to make sense of these parallel trends across disparate disciplines, I undertook a major survey about a decade ago. As part of that survey, my colleagues and I systematically examined findings from a host of disciplines and populations. We studied populations that exhibit unusual cognitive profiles, such as prodigies, autistic individuals, and people with learning disabilities. We looked at the kinds of psychological tests that correlated with one another, as well as those that did not. We examined the kinds of mental abilities that are valued in different cultures—the capacities exhibited by hunters, sailors, athletes, sorcerers, leaders, engineers, and musicians. Throughout the survey, we were on the lookout for those sets of abilities that could be found in different groups.

As a result of this wide-ranging survey, I arrived at a list of several human intelligences. It is my contention that, as a species, human beings have evolved over the millennia to carry out at least seven different and relatively autonomous kinds of information processing, or "ways of knowing." The first five are linguistic intelligence (of the sort exhibited by a poet, orator, or writer), logical-mathematical intelligence (a scientist, mathematician, or logician), musical intelligence (composer, performer, or sophisticated audience member), spatial intelligence (geometer, sculptor, artist, surgeon), and bodily-kinesthetic intelligence (athlete, dancer, mime, craftsperson). The last two are "personal" ways of knowing: Interpersonal intelligence (knowledge of other persons) is exhibited by teachers, clinicians, salespeople, and politicians, while intrapersonal intelligence (knowledge of oneself) characterizes individuals who have constructed a viable model of themselves and can operate effectively on the basis of that model. All human beings who are not grossly retarded have all of these potentials, but for both genetic and environmental reasons, individuals differ remarkably among themselves in the particular profiles of intelligence that they exhibit at any given moment and in how that profile might alter over time.

It turns out that cultures profit from these differences. We are able to "staff" our numerous roles and niches more effectively because people exhibit different profiles of intelligence. Even within a particular profession, one finds individuals with different blends of strength in areas such as language, logic, and interpersonal understanding. Now that the reasons that led to these differences in skill and inclination have become clearer, a uniform approach to education makes even less sense than it did before.

My belief in the importance—indeed, the necessity—of individual-centered education derives from two interlocking propositions. First of all, it has now been established convincingly that individuals have quite different minds from one another. Education ought to be so sculpted that it remains responsive to these differences. Instead of ignoring them, and pretending that all individuals have (or ought to have) the same kinds of minds, we should try to ensure that everyone receives an education that maximizes his or her own intellectual potential.

The second proposition is equally compelling. It may once have been true that a dedicated individual could master the world's extant knowledge, or at least some significant part of it. So long as this was a tenable goal, it made some sense to offer a uniform curriculum. Now, however, no individual can master even a single body of knowledge completely, let alone the range of disciplines and competences. The period of the Renaissance man or woman is long past. Inasmuch as choices of emphasis and scope *must* be made, the issue becomes only which path an individual should follow. The theory of multiple intelligences ought not to be used to dictate a course of study or career, but it constitutes a reasonable basis on which to make suggestions and to choose electives.

Once we decide to move away from uniform schooling, we need models that take seriously individual profiles of intelligence and seek to maximize the educational achievements of each person. I have in recent years devoted thought to how such an individual-centered school might be designed; and I have become involved in a number of experimental investigations that should ultimately indicate which of these models have merit. A convenient way to describe an individual-centered school is to delineate a set of roles that would be carried out within the school or school system.

A first role I have termed the "assessment specialist." It would be this person's task to provide a regularly updated view of the particular strengths, inclinations, and weaknesses of each student.

Such an assessment cannot be based primarily on standardized tests. According to my analysis, these instruments are inevitably biased in favor of two kinds of individuals: those with a particular blend of linguistic and logical intelligences and those who can succeed with instruments administered in a neutral, or "decontextualized," setting.

I believe that any new form of assessment needs to meet three criteria. It should be *intelligence-fair*—presented in a way so that the potency of an intelligence can be monitored directly, and not through the "lens" of logic and mathematics. It should be *developmentally appropriate*—using techniques suitable to the child's developmental level in the particular domain of knowledge at issue. It should be *linked to recommendations*—any score or description should be associated with recommended activities.

To make such an assessment, and to update it regularly, is obviously a major undertaking. Successful deployment depends upon teachers who are sensitive to the dimensions being examined and who can make pertinent observations while students are engaged in meaningful activities and projects. There remains a place for more focused interventions, using standardized instruments, but these should never be allowed to dominate assessment.

The assessment specialist would share findings and recommendations with students, parents, teachers, and the occupant of a second role, the "student-curriculum broker." On the basis of a current view of the student's intellectual profile, the broker would recommend which courses the student should elect and, even in the case of a uniform curriculum, how these materials are most likely to be mastered by the student.

To the extent that there are electives, it is pertinent for students to know their own strengths. However, this knowledge should not be used to dictate electives (a contradiction in terms). Rather, knowledge of one's own strengths can help one to choose courses that might be particularly congenial to one's learning style. In the case of a uniform or required curriculum, such information is equally important. For even if the courses themselves are mandated, they need not be taught in the same way at all.

In most areas of the curriculum, materials can be presented in a plethora of ways—by teachers or through books, software, hardware, or other media. The choice of mode of presentation can in many cases spell the differences between a successful and an unsuccessful educational experience. A history lesson can be presented through linguistic, logical, spatial, or personal modes of knowing, even as a geometry class can draw upon spatial, logical, linguistic, or numerical competences. Oftentimes some kind of cognitive prosthetic (for example, a computer program that allows the user to create a variety of spatial configurations) can help a student to master material that is difficult for her to envisage "in her own head." Now that we know something about teaching styles, learning styles, and individual intelligences, it is simply inexcusable to insist that all students learn the same thing in the same way.

A third role in the individual-centered school is the "school-community broker." Just as the student-curriculum broker would attempt to intercede on the student's behalf within the school walls, the school-community broker would search for educational opportunities for the student within a wider community.

In my own view, nothing is more important in a student's educational career than encountering a discipline or craft that fits a particular blend of intelligences—a pursuit worthy of a student's efforts for years or even a lifetime. Individuals of accomplishment often attribute enormous importance to "crystallizing experiences" where they first confronted a pursuit that fit their learning strengths and styles. All too often, these "matches" occurred completely by chance.

The goal of the school-community broker would be to increase the likelihood that each student will discover a vocational or avocational role that matches his own profile of intelligences. To accomplish this goal, the broker would assemble information about apprenticeships, mentorships, community organizations, and the like; each of these learning opportunities should exemplify a particular blend of intelligences. This information should be stored in some kind of a database and made available to interested students and parents.

Of course, any student could draw on the information culled by the school-community broker. However, the information would be particularly important for students who exhibit an unusual, "nonscholastic profile" of intelligences. After all, students with a blend of linguistic and logical intelligences are likely to do well in school, to evolve a positive self-image, and thus to feel less of a need for special counseling and for pursuing out-of-the-ordinary opportunities. On the other hand, for those students with unusual intellectual configurations, the school-community broker could provide the perhaps life-changing opportunity to engage in an activity that matches a specific configuration of talents.

It should be stressed that none of these roles is designed in any way to minimize or circumvent the role of the individual teacher. Indeed, such roles should free teachers to focus on their chosen subject matter and to present it in a way that is most comfortable for their own intellectual profiles. I envisage a special role for master teachers, who would ensure that the possibly idiosyncratic needs of individual students were being well served by the specialists and brokers who make educational recommendations.

Were such an individual-centered education to be pursued, it should lead to a happy situation—one in which an increasing percentage of students find their métier, feel better about themselves, and, perhaps, are more likely to become productive members of their community. Where there is only one standard of competence, it is virtually inevitable that most students will end up feeling incompetent; this is particularly true when that standard happens to favor a narrow band of intelligences. By openly embracing a wider range of end-states, and seeking to match intellectual profiles with educational opportunities, the individual-centered school increases the likelihood that students will achieve their maximum intellectual potential. I am pleased that these ideas fit comfortably with the long-term American ideals of progressive education—a form of education that is nowadays much maligned but that, when practiced well, is most consistent with societal values of pluralism, individuality, and cooperation for the greater good of all.

Though these recommendations represent a step in an "applied" direction, they were conceptualized largely in an ivory-tower setting. In recent years, however, my colleagues and I have become involved in efforts at a number of educational levels to guide education in an individual-centered direction. None of these experiments is far enough along to have claimed success (or conceded failure); but they do represent legitimate experiments that should eventually reveal the powers, as well as the limitations, of individual-centered education.

At the preschool level, my colleague David Feldman and I have devised an approach called Project Spectrum. Funded initially by the Spencer Foundation, the project was designed with a research question in mind: We wanted to determine whether children as young as three or four could already be distinguished from one another in terms of their respective profiles of intelligences. We have established to our satisfaction that children this young exhibit quite different intellectual profiles, and that it is simply wrong to classify them as more or less "smart." But at the same time, we have gone beyond the research issues that originally motivated the work.

Project Spectrum has become a full-fledged curricular and assessment effort in the preschool years. We have created a richly furnished environment designed to nourish the range of human intelligences. Children have the opportunity throughout the year to work with materials that stimulate diverse intelligences; from time to time, they are also engaged in more focused tasks that reveal more finely grained information about their unique intellectual profiles. Among the areas covered in Spectrum are storytelling, mechanical mastery, bodily expression, musical creation, and the child's understanding of the social world. At the end of the year we prepare a Spectrum Report on each child. This portrait of the child's strengths and weaknesses includes specific recommendations about what might be done at home, at school, or in the wider community to enhance the child's educational experience.

The enthusiastic response to Project Spectrum among preschool educators indicates that we have developed an educational regimen that makes sense for young children in our society. At the same time, we would like to believe that the kinds of information obtained by our unobtrusive assessment can be valuable to those who are later entrusted with the child's education and that weaknesses and deficiencies identified and addressed at this early juncture of life have a much greater chance of being ameliorated.

At the elementary school level, a group of teachers in Indianapolis have designed and placed into operation a so-called Key School—an experimental public school focused on developing in ordinary children the range of human intelligences. Each day students in this inner-city kindergarten-to-sixth-grade "option school" participate in classes that, taken together, address the full set of intelligences. Furthermore, and of particular interest here, is that students participate in an ensemble of novel activities devised to cut across, join together, or otherwise reconfigure their intellectual strengths.

One such activity is a "flow center," where students can select their own games and problem sets, and spend as long as they like with them. Another is the craft- or discipline-oriented "pods," where children of different ages work together as apprentices on an activity for which they have special interests or skills. The school also sponsors a set of three theme-related projects that are carried out over the course of the year by every student. These finished projects are put on display, and every child presents (and "defends") his or her project to the class and has the presentation videotaped.

As with Project Spectrum, it is still too early to determine the success of the Key School. Should its efforts be crowned with success, the credit will go entirely to the staff, parents, and administration of the school system—and not to me. Still, I am pleased that some of my individual-centered ideas have motivated this exceptionally interesting experiment.

At the middle and high school level, my associates at Harvard Project Zero and I have joined forces with colleagues at the Rockefeller Foundation, Educational Testing Service, and in the Pittsburgh public schools in an effort called Arts Propel (an acronym that denotes Production, Reflection, and Perception). We agree that however useful standardized tests may be in the "standard" areas of the curriculum, they are deficient in assessing potential and achievement in the arts and humanities. Consequently, the collaborators in Arts Propel seek to devise measures that can detect gifts and progress in visual arts, music, and imaginative writing in ordinary students.

As in Project Spectrum, what began as primarily an assessment enterprise has moved inexorably into curricular areas. The reason is simple. One cannot assess strengths unless students have had appreciable experience with the materials in question. But most students in American schools are not proficient at tasks and problems of consequence in the arts and humanities, such as composing a piece of music or writing a poem. Our efforts have accordingly centered on the creation of two new kinds of instruments, which we hope will prove useful in the Pittsburgh schools and perhaps elsewhere as well.

"Domain projects" are rich sets of exercises in a particular art form that attempt to teach concepts or skills central to that art form. A specimen musical domain project features the rehearsal of a work; one in the visual arts teaches students principles of style; one in imaginative writing introduces the process of writing dialogues in play. Reflecting our acronym, each exercise stresses production, but also includes aspects of perception and reflection. The assessment instruments we are designing fit hand in glove with the domain projects; thus, students as well as teachers will be able to monitor the learning that takes place.

Our second category of educational vehicles consists of collections of materials that document the planning and execution of full-scale artistic projects. We call these collections "portfolios," though the neologism "process-folio" may be a more accurate description. A portfolio includes the range of materials relevant to the execution of the project—opening plans, first drafts, initial evaluations, revisions, collections of works by others that are relevant to the project, final versions, and assessments by both the student who carried out the project and other knowledgeable persons. The portfolio serves as a detailed "cognitive map" of the student's learning over the course of the project.

Obviously, it is no easy matter to arrive at reliable means of evaluating a student's portfolio. We have to face the possibilities that there may be a significant subjective factor in such an evaluation and that universal standards may prove elusive. At the same time, we are confident that we will be able to evaluate some facets of portfolios in an objective manner. Moreover, I feel strongly that the sheer exercise of assembling and evaluating a portfolio will be an extremely valuable educational opportunity, one worth pursuing even apart from the attainment of impeccable scoring mechanisms.

Let me mention some reasons for my enthusiasm about portfolio methods. First, I believe that it is through such sustained activities that students get the most reliable sense of what it is like to be deeply involved with an artistic medium. Second, these activities are more likely than standard classroom activities to bring to the fore the student's individual interests, his or her creativity and distinctive "voice," and the chance that the student can contribute to problem formation as well as problem solution.

There is an additional reason for my enthusiasm, one of particular moment in the United States today. In the current educational context, most students receive little or no reinforcement for regular and steady involvement in an activity over a significant period of time. Indeed, owing to the biases of uniform education, students are overloaded with assignments and tests that are atomistic, particularistic, short-answer, and usually unconnected to sustained goals. Any activities that can help to repair this imbalance—so damaging, and so misleading as to what "counts" once one leaves the grounds of school—should be held at a particular premium.

The portfolio can be useful in evaluating learning and progress in the arts and humanities. In addition, I submit, it can be a particularly valuable part of the dossier that students submit to college admissions officers—a dossier that can document learning in science or social science as well. In my view, the capacity of students to carry out sustained projects, and to document them in pertinent ways, is an extremely valuable piece of information, which may well have strong predictive value about success in school and success beyond school.

In fact, I would wager that when considered together with high school record and recommendations, portfolio information would be *more* valuable than scores on standardized tests. I have been informally challenging admissions officers at major schools to encourage submission of this kind of information. Such a receptiveness would send a strong and needed message to high schools about activities that ought to be more strongly encouraged—sustained projects that are rewarding in their own right, that develop invaluable skills, and that give students a feeling for the kinds of performances needed once they leave the cloisters of college.

I am pleased that the above experiments are being carried out—all involved will learn from them. Nevertheless, it is timely to point out that the approach growing out of multiple intelligences is by no means free of problems, and that it has left unaddressed a number of consequential issues.

To begin with, there is a danger of "premature billeting." If a student seems gifted in the bodily-kinesthetic area, for example, parents or teachers might decide to push strongly for that student to become a dancer, athlete, or craftsperson. Such a move would be unfortunate for two reasons. First, there is no evidence that signs of early strength necessarily predict ultimate career satisfaction; if anything, early profiles are quite flexible, and there is no reason to accept them as a necessary recipe for the future. Second, in addition to its being questionable on scientific grounds, I challenge the general value of early billeting. Students ought to have the opportunity to pursue as many options as they like. Early information about strengths or weaknesses should be used principally to define students' options more clearly and to give them the chance to shore up weaknesses, should they seek to do so.

There is no guaranteed way in which a researcher can prevent the abuse of his or her findings, of course. The best alternative is to provide positive models of how the information about intellectual profiles can be used to increase options, rather than to foreclose them.

A number of profound issues are also bracketed by the theory of multiple intelligences, two of which have particularly preoccupied me of late. One has to do with how to balance the need for developing *basic skills* during childhood with the desire to preserve and enhance a child's *creativity*. The second has to do with the need for some *common core of knowledge* among all individuals within a polity, as against the rival good of recognizing the *plurality of human cultures* and of allowing students to pursue their own areas of special interests and aptitudes.

It would be disastrous to take an unmodulated perspective on either of these issues. We cannot and should not proceed completely in the direction of basic skills, even as we cannot and should not wholly embrace creativity. By the same token, we should not opt for a completely common curriculum any more than we should offer un-limited electives at all ages and under all circumstances.

But can we go beyond a simple plea, or recipe, for a balance between creativity and skills, or between generalized and specialized knowledge? I believe that we can. To do so requires two steps. First, we need to think of the optimal educational regimen as shifting between periods that favor different ideals. Second, while pursuing any one goal, it is essential that we keep in view, and available as a viable option, the other goal as well.

Each culture needs to work out the preferred balance in a way appropriate to its own means and goals. My view is that the preferred route for American society is to shift emphases at a number of points during education. For a child's first seven years, there should be considerable free choice and much fostering of creativity. The following seven years—the initial years of formal schooling—should be characterized by increased emphasis on the development of skills and the embracing of significant common curricula. The following period, roughly from high school through undergraduate education, should include electives, courses that cut across traditional disciplinary backgrounds, and innovative problem forming and problem solving. Finally, to balance this regimen, the period of professional training should again emphasize skills and problem solving.

Obviously, this formula is simple—if not simplistic—and needs to be modulated. Also, I must stress even while one educational end is being emphasized, it is crucial to keep the contrasting options in mind. Thus, the notion of alternative answers to a problem should be stressed during the skill-building period of the early school years; by the same token, the importance of pursuing a craft needs to be emphasized even during the cross-disciplinary years of college. Nonetheless, the notion of a "cycle of emphases" does represent one promising way to achieve a balance between competing but equally desirable educational goals. Moreover, as I argue at length in my recent book *To Open Minds*,[3] it is a regimen that makes sense both in terms of scientific knowledge about human development and in terms of educational values that are widely shared in our country.

I am open to criticisms and reservations about individual-centered education and, indeed, have brought up several in these pages. But there is one critique I unequivocally reject: the claim that individual-centered education is utopian. As this view is customarily expressed, it is simply too expensive and unwieldy to try to construct education around the particular strengths and inclinations of individual children; consequently, even if there are some principled merits to the individual-centered approach, they must be set aside in favor of an approach that is more cost-efficient, "competitive," or practical. And thus, on pragmatic if not scientific or value grounds, we must embrace a uniform approach to education.

To my mind, the real obstacles to individual-centered education are not financial constraints or knowledge limitations but rather *questions of will*. So long as we choose to believe that this approach is not valid or, even if valid, simply not practical, it will *appear* utopian. If, however, we decide to embrace the goals and the methods of individual-centered education, I have no doubt that we can make significant progress in that direction.

One reason for my optimism are the various educational experiments described above. They are all modest projects that could be undertaken with minor budgetary adjustments in any school system. Moreover, once a model had been devised, it is not necessary to repeat the various experimental phases and errors; it should therefore become more possible to achieve the goals of individual-centered education without breaking the bank.

What is necessary, rather, is the willingness of members of the wider community to participate in such experiments. So long as problems are thrown squarely into the laps of teachers and school administrators, and the rest of the community shuns all involvement, we will be destined to promote inadequate education, whether of the uniform or the individual stripe. Community organizations must be willing to host students as apprentices; parents must be willing to help out in preschools and elementary schools, and to attend meetings at which their children's progress is discussed; college faculty must be willing to look at portfolios rather than relegate all work to admissions officers who (of necessity) simply abide by cutoff scores on standardized tests. If each individual in the community is willing to tithe but a modicum of time or money, however, individual-centered goals can be readily attained.

With support from the political leaders of our country, with the growing professionalization of teachers and administrators, with the increasing involvement of students themselves in their own educational career choices, a shift to individual-centered education could be quite readily accomplished. As I have argued in these pages, such a move would make eminent sense in two respects: On the scientific level, an education that takes seriously individual differences in intellectual strengths and inclinations is responsive to our emerging knowledge about the human mind. On the level of values, an education that takes seriously the different strengths and proclivities of our citizens is consonant with the deepest American values—and directly undermines the totalitarian implications of a uniform education. Unlike the weather, American education *is* amenable to change—and the moment for us to change it is clearly at hand.

NOTES

[1] Howard Gardner, *Frames of Mind: The Theory of Multiple Intelligences* (New York: Basic Books, 1983).

[2] Howard Gardner, *The Mind's New Science* (New York: Basic Books, 1985).

[3] Howard Gardner, *To Open Minds: Chinese Clues to the Dilemma of Contemporary Education* (New York: Basic Books, 1989).

Video, Memory, and Computers

PAUL RYAN

. . . there is no way to call off the liaison between video and computers. But there are other connections to be made with video that could keep the video-computer hybrid from becoming a loose cannon on the rolling deck of memory. What I have in mind is developing patterns that connect video with perception, ecology, mortality, and relationships.

Recently, Sony Corporation ran an ad for its Handycam video camera that targeted middle-aged, male baseball fans. The close-up photo shows an old bat, a ball, a glove, and a Handycam. On the ball you can read the inscription, 1958 City Champs. The boldface ad copy below the picture reads: "They all bring back memories of your old baseball pals. But with the Sony, there won't be a single error." The rest of the ad bemoans the fact that the reader of the ad can't recall some of the players on his championship team and instructs him to purchase a Handycam so his son can relive *his* baseball memories free of error. The copy ends, "The Sony Handycam. It's everything you want to remember."

Video is a technology of memory. There are other technologies of memory. Other ways to create a "remembrance of things past." It will be a while before video finds its Proust, but the need is already evident in Sony's ad. The ad is symptomatic of what happens when video caters to "everything you want to remember." Celebrating video as error-free memory has its pitfalls. Simply by selecting material for later showing, the camera person "conceals" other material that may be important to remember.

What about the involuntary memory Proust cultivated? What about those things you may not want to remember but *need* to remember? Is not catering to desirable memories a prescription for living in a video cocoon of nostalgia? What is the consequence of preselected memory? How can we remember what we conceal with the camera? What happens to perception if the camera is used primarily to gather material for memory—does it not atrophy? Moreover, the old baseball glove may have a smell that triggers memories video simply cannot match—what about them?

A full understanding of video and memory would require a rigorous comparison between video and other technologies of memory, such as oral recitation, print, and holography. It would also require linking these technologies to the human sensorium. Such a study is beyond the scope of what can be accomplished here. In this exploratory essay, I can only suggest ways of approaching the issue of video and memory. I begin by focusing on the fact that video memory is currently being joined with another odorless memory technology, the computer. After twenty years of experience with video, I am nervous about this marriage of convenience. Let me say why.

Computers digitize knowledge: They transform it into information stored in binary units. Once knowledge is digitized, it can be manipulated in an incredible range of ways. For example, video images are now being digitized and manipulated by computer to show people what they would look like if they wore this or that hairstyle. Computers can alter photos or simulate video images of real things in ways that are undetectable. In itself, this is a technological achievement to be applauded. But soon we will no longer be able to trust that the recognizable image on videotape was made when someone pointed the camera at something real.

I'm not against the simulation of possibilities by computers. I think imagining possibilities is all to the good, especially if it involves all the complexity at our command with computers. My concern is that the computerization of video information will detach video images from reference to what we see in our daily lives. Odorless electronic memory systems will create powerful information banks in arbitrary digital storage devices with no grounding in the world familiar to our senses.

So what to do? Obviously, there is no way to call off the liaison between video and computers. But there are other connections to be made with video that could keep the video-computer hybrid from becoming a loose cannon on the rolling deck of memory. What I have in mind is developing patterns that connect video with perception, ecology, mortality, and relationships. In so doing, we can help ensure that the mediation of memory by video in a computerized culture does not trap us in a smog of digitized nostalgia but helps us gain some freedom for a human future.

A video camera enables you to push the envelope of your perception beyond anything premeditated. Because the video recorder assumes full responsibility for remembering what is perceived, the video-maker can take perceptual risks: He or she can forget to remember what is being perceived and cultivate a Zen state of watchfulness for whatever can be found through the viewfinder.

While this watchfulness can also be cultivated to some extent with film, other factors come into play with video. I am thinking of the alpha state of brain waves associated with the electronics of television for videomaker and viewer alike. One pioneer video artist, Al Robbins, now deceased, developed a technique of punctuating the tape he shot with trigger cuts every few seconds. He explains this technique as a way to keep himself from becoming mindlessly fascinated by what he saw in the viewfinder—as if he were repeatedly slapping himself on the head to make sure he wasn't dreaming. Robbins did not trust the Zen/alpha state. He cultivated a meta-Zen state. The beauty of the tapes he made demonstrates that meta-Zen is not a contradiction in terms, at least in the case of Al Robbins. He kept his mind active and alive behind the camera by constantly interrupting himself. To watch his tapes is to learn a different way of seeing.

In my own tape making, I developed a different approach. I learned t'ai chi ch'uan and developed a handheld camera style based on continuous t'ai chi movements. The t'ai chi enabled me to "meditate in motion" through the camera. I was challenged by the sheer capacity for duration of perception a half hour or more of videotape makes possible. About twelve years ago I did thirty-six continuous half-hour tapes in a variety of sites, t'ai chi–style, without any trigger cuts. I was pushing the envelope of video perception, trusting the camera to remember for me. My Zen state was not perfect, but good enough that I could "be there" for maybe eighteen minutes of a half-hour tape done while standing in the middle of water flowing over rock. It was a quite wonderful thing to do. I was able to free my perceptions from the burden of memory and attach my attention to flowing water. I doubt if any computer could simulate the singularity of such perceptual risk taking. Moreover, the video record of what I saw could be shared with others. Video invites the development of a whole range of such techniques for enlivening perceptions.

As a species, humanity has two ways to transmit information over generations. One is through the genetic code; the other is through speech and writing. Speech and writing inevitably involve authority structures, somebody telling somebody else what to do. "No, don't touch. The oven is hot," says the parent. The developing integrity of the child's perceptual system is broken into, and behavior is linked up to the language commands of adults. Language commands from competing authority figures often leave us caught in contradictions. After a study of modern painters, particularly Monet, the biologist C. H. Waddington argued that it may be possible to develop an information transmission system married to the perception of environmental realities and not to speech and writing. Such a system would be nonarbitrary and free of the contradictions of competing language authorities. Video gives us the possibility of making such a marriage by generalizing what modern painters sweated blood to do: to see the environment without words.

Whether it's a ball game, a beauty pageant, a presidential funeral, or the launch of a spacecraft, video lets us monitor events simultaneously with others. Video holds the memory of such events as monitored. The ecology is an ensemble of recurring events: tides changing, leaves falling, birds migrating, and so on. Video can be used systematically to monitor the recurring events of a local ecology for the people who live in that ecology.

The traditional technology of oral memory worked in terms of what are called commonplaces. Every schoolchild in Shakespeare's day wrote an essay on "To be or not to be." There was a finite set of recurring themes to which everybody referred, which was the glue that held the community together.

The recurring ecological events that are common to a place could, in fact, become the commonplaces of an electronic memory. Falsification of these commonplaces by computer would be very difficult, since people could go out and have a look for themselves anytime they wanted. Video could record and store these events as they recurred, and changed, over generations. Marrying our electronic memories to the ongoing perceptible events of the ecology would give us a reliable reference system, free of the arbitrariness and contradictions possible with digitized, computerized authority. With an electronic memory married to ongoing ecological events, human mortals would stand a better chance of thriving from generation to generation. Such a memory system may even help us regenerate our despoiled planet. Once such a memory system was in place, computers could be used to simulate the consequences of different policies and practices for our ecological systems, before we risked implementing them.

The species that destroys its ecology destroys itself. Clearly, humans can now destroy the ecologies of the earth. We are an endangered species. This status changes our approach to immortality: No human is immortal if the species goes extinct.

"Immortality" depends on the human practice of remembering the dead. This practice is part of what makes us human. Different cultures have remembered their dead in ways that range from the burial mounds of Native Americans to the realistic busts of the Romans. With video we have the image of the deceased "live on tape." Such an image is much more powerful than any computer simulation of a person or any computer readout about a person's life. As home video becomes increasingly diffused through the culture, more and more people will be dealing with the fact of death remembered through video replay of a deceased family member. How do we configure the emotions unique to this new condition?

My sense is that we need to ritualize video replay of the dead. The video presence of a deceased loved one can be overwhelming and severely disorienting. It is one thing to chance across a photo of you and a loved one now gone. It is another to find yourself live on tape with someone you loved, now deceased, during a replaying of random videotapes. Ritual sets up a situation where emotions can be experienced in a crisis-proof context, one that is usually supplied by a secure cosmology, an overarching story in which the life of the deceased finds meaning and that meaning is shared by the living. In this context of shared meaning, emotions of loss can be fully experienced. The fact that we are now an endangered species has shaken the security of every traditional context of shared meaning. We need to develop a new cosmology, a new story that reckons with our ecological situation and allows us to organize our relationships accordingly. It seems to me that only in the context of such a new story can we invent stable rituals that allow us to replay the dead live on tape. Given the flexibility of electronic information technologies, we have the possibility of telling the story in a nonnarrative way that avoids the patterns of dominance associated with logocentric "master narratives." Another way of saying this is that we can encode cosmology in a way that is sensitive to chaos and responsive to local knowledge.

Depth psychology is said to have begun with photography. I think video is initiating a new dimension of understanding that as yet has no formal name or discipline. But it has to do with relationships, ways of interacting, the sorts of issues that family therapists have worked with since the fifties.

As we work to find proper ways to balance our relationships with the living, we will continue to suffer the deaths of those we love and hold live on tape. Records of interaction kept in a family over generations could help untangle family knots, keep the children from repeating the errors of their parents. Maybe.

Humans care about their relationships. Birth and death are catastrophes that drastically change patterns of relationships. Video replay offers us a way to help balance relationships among the living. This possibility was never more apparent to me than in an extraordinary video experiment I made with a friend.

My friend and I recorded a conversation between us using full-body shots on a split screen. We were seated facing each other. A week later we played the tape back using slow motion and no sound. We sat facing the screen, each of us imitating the gestures of the other on the screen and creating conversation on the basis of the motions. Holding my head and rocking back and forth in imitation of my friend, I found myself saying, "Yeah. I'm listening to what you're saying, Ryan, but I'm really getting ready to strike back." Following my imitation of a diminutive hand gesture, I said, "Let me make it nice and small, Ryan, so that you can understand it." My friend was articulating my nonverbal attitudes in a similar way, and we were laughing our heads off. What was even more extraordinary was that when I woke up the next morning, I felt as if I were wearing his body. I called him up and started telling him how I felt about the relation between his/my stomach and shoulders, stomach and torso, torso and legs, and so forth. In each case he confirmed that my feeling was accurate. For the next few weeks I could recall the sense of his body whenever I wanted. Video replay had made possible an extraordinary degree of imitation and empathy. Such empathy can make a real difference in balancing relationships, well beyond that made by computerized programs of interaction.

Developing patterns that connect video with perception, ecology, mortality, and relationships can neutralize possible adverse effects of the current video-computer hybrid. To work positively with this hybrid, we need to understand the fundamental difference between video and computers, which can be characterized by two words: complexity and contiguity. Computers enable us to order electronically a multiplicity of parts into a whole—that is, they extend our capacity to deal with complexity. Video, on the other hand, extends our capacity to deal with contiguity, the state of being in actual contact. Addressing contiguity will enable us to better understand the possible falsification of memory inherent in video itself. Heidegger's account of memory is useful here:

> Originally, a "memory" means . . . a constant, concentrated abiding with something—not with something that has passed, but in the same way with what was present and with what may come. [1]

> Only because we are by nature gathered in contiguity can we remain concentrated on what is at once present, past and to come. The word "memory" originally meant this incessant concentration on contiguity. [2]

We are in actual, continuous contact with both the past and the future. We are continually gathering ourselves together in terms of what just happened and what will happen next. This is what Heidegger means by saying that "we are by nature gathered in contiguity." Contiguity is a key to understanding video and memory. Videomaking puts you in conscious contact with contiguity. A number of videomakers, myself included, are so struck by this condition that we insist on the value of continuous taping because it trains the mind in contiguity. What is originally felt as boredom develops into a capacity for concentration on what is past, present, and to come.

Contiguity helps explain other techniques of videomaking, such as fading one tape into another rather than making jump cuts, extensive use of slow motion, replaying tapes in reverse, and creating multi-monitor pieces that deal with different temporal patterns. The relationship between video and contiguity is especially evident in the work of video artist Gary Hill. Hill did a videotape that is a dramatic rendering of a metalogue between the communication theorist Gregory Bateson and his daughter Catherine. (A metalogue is a conversation about some problematic subject in which the structure of the conversation is also relevant to the subject.) Hill taught the actors who performed the metalogue to say the words backward for the video performance. He then edited this performance tape to correct this initial misorientation. He ran their backward talk forward. What the viewer heard was a strange-sounding but discernible performance of the metalogue. What the viewer saw was an interactive sequence in reverse. As the Bateson character puffs on his pipe, the smoke keeps curling back into the pipe. Hill's multiple reversals of time's arrow celebrate contiguity with an indifference toward the past and the future.

Of course, such editing of the past, present, and future is an artistic construct, not an actuality. Video makes the construct possible. The actual past and the actual future do not allow us to be indifferent to them. As we have seen in discussing mortality, the past is never more clearly the past than when we think about the dead. Those absent from us are absent, even if we have them live on tape. Death makes absence final. The brutal fact is that the dead are forever gone from us; our life with them took place in the past. The appreciation for contiguity inherent in video should not confuse this fact. Indeed, the appreciation of contiguity via video is not automatic. The contiguity of video ought not be confused with the contiguity of life itself.

Just as literacy has given us an enormous appreciation of language, so video can give us an enormous appreciation of contiguity. Unfortunately, literacy has blinded us to some of the consequences of its silent sequencing. It would be well to be as circumspect as possible about the consequences of video.

As we saw with regard to the Sony ad, there is a way in which video replay can create a false sense of the past for videomakers and viewers alike. This is true even if the camera work is not predetermined. There is a tendency to remember only those aspects of events that have been recorded and replayed. The video replay begins to be the criterion for what is worth remembering and what is not worth remembering about events.

In addition to falsifying the past, video replay can falsify the sense of the present. In my own experience, after extensive replay of events involving human interaction—conversations, dancing, car travel—I began to expect that all human interactions were replayable. Unconsciously I was thinking, Why get fully involved in whatever was going on? Save some emotion for enjoying (and examining) the replay. After all, an unexamined life is not worth living, and video allows us to examine life very closely. It took losing a close friend to reestablish my appreciation for unrepeatable, irreversible events in life.

The possibility of video's creating confusion about the present is especially evident in instant replay, which can blur the difference between present and past. This is clear in video art that uses open-reel recorders. The open reel allows replay after a delay of only a few seconds. The trick is simple: Put two video decks side by side. Because the tapes are not on cassettes, it is possible to thread one tape through both machines. You can then record on the first machine and play back on the second. Two artists, Frank Gillette and Ira Schneider, used this technique very effectively at the Howard Wise Gallery show "TV as a Creative Medium" (1969). The piece they did for the show "Wipe Cycle" was complex. I will describe only the aspect of it that helps us to understand instant replay.

The first machine recorded people as they stepped off the elevator into the gallery. The second machine replayed the event to these same people eight seconds later, on a television set in the gallery. Under normal circumstances, having an elevator door close behind you is an event that separates the past from the present. With the eight-second replay, however, past and present became confused; the past did not detach itself from the present. Video extended the sense of the present (being in the gallery) to include the past (being in the elevator) and an event that normally separates the two (stepping off the elevator and having the door close behind you).

To say it another way, instant replay established a continuity over a threshold that was normally a discontinuity. By recording and replaying the passage from one space to another, the artists scrambled the normal distribution of past and present. Strange. People stood watching themselves coming out of an elevator eight seconds ago, absorbing a past that had not been detached from the present.

It is this nondetachment of the past from the present that characterizes what we call instant replay. With instant replay the sense of the present can be extended far beyond eight seconds. Recording the kids opening Christmas presents and then playing the tape back before the excitement dies down can take a good hour. The hour is experienced in one gestalt that includes instant replay.

Video can include the past in a present that grows into the future. Using video to gain some freedom for a human future depends on deepening our understanding of contiguity. In a computerized culture without an understanding of contiguity, the danger is that the power of the computer to calculate complexity will be used to colonize the future. Life will not be allowed to unfold for the young. Managing time will become the be-all and end-all. Even now people have no time—no time for the memories that come with the smells of everyday, no time for friends, no time for family, no time for pain.

Computers cultivate an appreciation for complexity. Video cultivates an appreciation for contiguity. The question becomes this: How do we gather the wisdom to develop a culture that appreciates *both* complexity *and* contiguity?

NOTES

[1] Martin Heidegger, *What Is Thinking?* (New York: Harper & Row, 1968), p. 140.

[2] Ibid., p. 145.

Fiction—Its Uses and Misuses

MARK JAY MIRSKY

Generally it is the willingness of the writer of fiction to be lost in his or her work, to suffer a vertigo that abandons method, that gives the prose its uncanny hold, as if a life had been thrown into the works like some primitive sacrifice—therefore Thoreau's cruel jibe has a certain justice, that no valuable work is accomplished except "at the expense of a life."

Theories of fiction are rarely congenial to writers of fiction—though some novelists (I am thinking of E. M. Forster and Henry James) have seemed to enjoy detailing if not a philosophy, a logistics, of fiction. And their work on the subject is interesting, although they say most in those gnomic utterances, their epigrams. Generally it is the willingness of the writer of fiction to be lost in his or her work, to suffer a vertigo that abandons method, that gives the prose its uncanny hold, as if a life had been thrown into the works like some primitive sacrifice—therefore Thoreau's cruel jibe has a certain justice, that no valuable work is accomplished except "at the expense of a life."

I will yield to the temptation to take up an old argument with a partially invisible adversary.

> Mark J. Mirsky writes a manifesto for a new periodical called *Fiction* devoted to reviving the art in the 1970's and he says: "We simply cannot believe that people have tired of stories, that the ear of America has atrophied permanently and is now deaf to myth, fable, puzzle, paradox." "In the mythos," he says, quoting Thoreau, "a superhuman intelligence uses the unconscious thoughts of men as its hieroglyphics to address men unborn."
>
> Nothing could have been further from the minds of the realists who established the novel as the reigning genre over a hundred years ago. As a matter of fact, they were turning their backs, with a kind of mucker's euphoria, on the idea of myth and fable, which had been the revered tradition of classical verse and French- and Italian-style court literature. It is hard to realize today just how drenched in realism the novel was at the outset—*le réalisme pour le réalisme*—*all this is true to life!* Defoe presents *Robinson Crusoe* as the actual memoir of a shipwrecked sailor. [1]

So wrote Tom Wolfe, then high priest of the New Journalism, in *Esquire* in 1972. Wolfe's citing Daniel Defoe as the ultimate example of the novelist as journalist, the reporter of social detail, piqued me.

The image of the solitary man—that is, man mastering his environment, man as manipulator in a solitary world—is the real attraction
of Defoe for us, not his journalism. It is also the reason why *Walden,* of
all of Thoreau's books, has had the most hypnotic effect on the
generations who have read him.

Under the pastoral of *Walden* thrums the beat of Greek tragedy and
its myth—the notion of incest as a return to a perfect world, an
idealized childhood where mother and son, father and daughter, are
locked in a symbiosis never to be broken by death. These dreams,
carried into the adult world, are part of that questioning of time that
the novelist carries on. Defoe, in fact, created in his great character
Robinson Crusoe one of the first modern heroes, a man who would
eccentrically re-create paradise, a male paradise, before woman, before the separation of the rib. From another perspective. Crusoe is
Homo faber, the fabricator of his own paradise. (It is interesting in this
context to note that Max Frisch's *Homo Faber* is exactly about the
return to innocence through incest.)

We are surrounded by taboos, and rightly so. It is not permissible
to talk about attraction to one's children in respectable journalism—
doing so is to suggest that it is permissible, and that is heinous. Yet it
is impossible to avoid the dreams and the dangers of incest—and that
is one of the hypnotic effects of *King Lear* as I watch the old man
struggle with the eroticism of deep old age. As I thought about
Hamlet after the death of my own father, sitting at a cafe in Buenos
Aires, the world tipped upside down, it seemed to me that the play
was about Hamlet's father's will to draw his son down into the grave,
and that we saw this, in fact, when Hamlet through the skull of
Yorick jests with his own father's bleak will. The play and the counter-
play, the buried play, so to speak.

There are two possibilities open to the novelist: to entertain, or to
try to understand and draw the outline of the world as it is suspected
from dreams and from the accretion of daily outrage and frustration.
It is always dangerous. It recalls the Cuban poet Padilla's words,
"Don't forget it, poet. . . . always, lurking in ambush, the dangerous
poem." Even as society and the media trumpet racial justice, for
instance, the novelist observes all around him the abuse of race by its

very victims who are using it as an excuse to be sadistic, lazy, even criminal. In like fashion the Holocaust is made a convenient crying pillow for gonifs, charlatans, the self-righteous. Yet the gusto of the faker, the liar, the cheat, his illusionary world, is almost a thing of beauty to a novelist. It is to the issue of the future that the fiction I care about addresses itself. Among fellow writers of difficult fiction I often heard the word *experimental,* and I winced; but I was glad, I will confess, of any company, so I didn't sigh too openly. It was the work of deliberately self-deluded writers—Dante, Thoreau, someone dreaming of writing as possession, as exploration of the limits, death, sex, politics—that attracted me, not a formal experiment. Dante's sexual persona was important because he was a full man, a man involved politically and religiously, so that what he reported of a possible sexual life and where it brought him in the universe, in both anxiety and dream, served as signposts for me. It seemed to me as important as Freud. Freud himself recognized that in front of a writer like Dostoevsky, the tension of laughter, self-cruelty, and admission made scientific method as such difficult if not irrelevant, and he proposed that analysis lay down its "arms." In fiction one grasped the world through sympathy.

This is all so nonspecific. There is a story by Bruno Schulz, which gives the title to his second collection in English, *Sanatorium Under the Sign of the Hourglass.* It spoke to me so eerily of my father's death—though he was not dead when I read it—that it has seemed to me ever since a deep and consoling chapter of philosophy, of dream logic, making clear my experience—the irrational as I felt it in the face of a parent's death.

> The journey was long. The train, which ran once a week on that forgotten branch line, carried no more than a few passengers. Never before had I seen such archaic coaches; withdrawn from other lines long before; they were spacious as living rooms, dark and with many recesses. Corridors crossed the empty compartments at various angles; labyrinthine and cold, they exhibited an air of strange and frightening neglect. I moved from coach to coach, looking for a comfortable corner. Drafts were everywhere: cold currents of air shooting through the interiors, piercing the whole train from end to end. Here and there

a few people sat on the floor, surrounded by their bundles, not daring
to occupy the empty seats. Beside, those high, convex, oilcloth-
covered seats were cold as ice and sticky with age. At the deserted
stations no passengers boarded the train. Without a whistle, without a
groan, the train would start again, as if lost in meditation.

This improbable train, so specifically Polish a train on a branch line to
nowhere, leads to a sanatorium, hidden in an enormous park, through
a landscape drained of color, "a cloudy summer dusk . . . saturated
with water after a long period of rain." The setting "exudes a feeling of
self-denial, a resigned and ultimate numbness that does not need the
consolation of color." Even the leaves of the trees here are "dark,
almost black. It was a strangely charged blackness, deep and benevo-
lent, like restful sleep." In the sanatorium, escorted by a lewd nurse
wiggling her hips, sex and death somehow synonymous, the narrator
meets the doctor, and the question of the story bursts immediately to
his lips.

> "Is my father alive?" I asked, staring anxiously into his calm face.
> "Yes, of course," he answered calmly, meeting my questioning eyes.
> "That is, within the limits imposed by the situation," he added, half
> closing his eyes. "You know as I that from the point of view of your
> home, from the perspective of your own country, your father is dead.
> This cannot be entirely remedied. That death throws a certain shadow
> on his existence here."
> "But does Father himself know it? Does he guess?" I asked him in a
> whisper.
> He shook his head with a deep conviction. "Don't worry," he said in
> a low voice. "None of our patients know it, or can guess. . . ."

This beginning poses a problem that obsessed Maimonides, Aquinas,
and Dante (and which was the theme of the *Commedia*): "the state of
souls after death, pure and simple," as Dante wrote Can Grande, his
patron. There is nothing, of course, simple about what we imagine
the state of death to be. Schulz constructs a world in which a dead
father can be recovered, but only within a situation that is dreamlike
and finally intolerable, from which the narrator flees. I put down the

story with the uncanny sense that I had visited a dream of my own, one in which I was allowed beyond the boundary of the dead. That we are allowed passage to the world of the dead, but only "within the limits imposed by the situation," is what Odysseus realizes in Homer's *Odyssey*, as he struggles to hold his mother in the realm of death and gasps air. Virgil repeats this several times in the *Aeneid*, with the same sense of personal pathos. It is to this particular problem that I believe the whole of Dante's *Commedia* is addressed, the substance of the dead—in particular, of a woman the poet has decided to embrace, and to make love to, have sex with, in death. What kind of a body can he expect? The answers of the poem, the fiction, are all drawn from philosophy, from the texts of Augustine, the church fathers, Maimonides, Plotinus. In a novella, *Dorchester, Home and Garden,* long before I had really grappled with Dante's text, given the touchstone of Harry Austryn Wolfson's extraordinary *The Souls of the Spheres,* I went searching for my mother among the dead with a company of philosophers under the Copley Square Library, my underground, the Boston Tarturus.

"You think that your mother's still around?"
"Please, please." I was crying.
"If you just want her to be around, that's enough. Immortality, resurrection . . ." he sang to a show tune. "You can't have one . . . without the ah . . . ah . . . aahther!
"O.K.," he winked, "cheered up?"[2]

Immortality leads us back to childhood, and to a familiar terrain, the childhood of our consciousness, of the religious literature that has colored our language, our way of thinking, our dread. It is the garden, the specific garden, that rises to Kafka's lips as the very condition of man in his correspondence with the Czech woman Milena, where Kafka agonizes over their forbidden love.

You write about the people who have their evenings and mornings together and those who haven't. Just the position of the letter seems to me the more favorable. . . . nothing decisive has happened, nothing really decisive in Heaven or on Earth, it's actually nothing but a "play

with a ball," as you call it. It's as though Eve, having indeed plucked
the apple from the tree (sometimes I believe I understand the Fall of
Man as no one else), did so nevertheless only in order to show it to
Adam—because she liked it. It was the biting into it that was
decisive—the playing with it was, though not permitted, not forbidden either.[3]

It is curious that Milan Kundera, in his obsession with the story of the
garden, focuses on defecation. For him, it would seem, the story of
the garden is the ultimate kitsch.

Shit is a more onerous theological problem than is evil. Since God gave
man freedom, we can, if need be, accept the idea that He is not
responsible for man's crimes. The responsibility for shit, however, rests
entirely with Him, the Creator of man.

In the fourth century, Saint Jerome completely rejected the notion
that Adam and Eve had sexual intercourse in Paradise. On the other
hand, Johannes Scotus Erigena, the great ninth-century theologian,
accepted the idea. He believed, moreover, that Adam's virile member
could be made to rise like an arm or a leg, when and as its owner
wished. We must not dismiss this fancy as the recurrent dream of a
man obsessed with the threat of impotence. Erigena's idea has a different meaning. If it were possible to raise the penis by means of a
simple command, then sexual excitement would have no place in the
world. The penis would rise not because we are excited but because we
order it to do so. What the great theologian found incompatible with
Paradise was not sexual intercourse and the attendant pleasure; what he
found incompatible with Paradise was excitement. Bear in mind:
There was pleasure in Paradise, but no excitement.

Erigena's argument holds the key to a theological justification (in
other words, a theodicy) of shit. As long as man was allowed to remain
in Paradise, either (like Valentinus' Jesus) he did not defecate at all, or
(as would seem more likely) he did not look upon shit as something
repellent. Not until after God expelled man from Paradise did He
make him feel disgust. Man began to hide what shamed him, and by
the time he removed the veil, he was blinded by a great light. Thus,
immediately after his introduction to disgust, he was introduced to
excitement. Without shit (in both the literal and figurative senses of

the word), there would be no sexual love as we know it, accompanied
by pounding heart and blinded senses.

In Part Three of this novel I told the tale of Sabina standing half-
naked with a bowler hat on her head and the fully dressed Tomas at her
side. There is something I failed to mention at the time. While she was
looking at herself in the mirror, excited by her self-denigration, she
had a fantasy of Tomas seating her on the toilet in her bowler hat and
watching her void her bowels. Suddenly her heart began to pound and,
on the verge of fainting, she pulled Tomas down to the rug and
immediately let out an orgasmic shout. [4]

It is difficult to know whether Kundera has his tongue in cheek or
not. Many centuries before Erigena, Augustine had spoken about the
sexual act in the garden. For some theologians this was a crucial
question—as it implied either a curse or a blessing on procreation.
Sadly, *The Unbearable Lightness of Being* suggests a curse on procreation. Both the novel's imagery and its distinction, pleasure but no
excitement without excrement, while pretending to be a celebration
of life and earthiness, conceal an implicit distaste for childbearing. It
is the question of "eternal recurrence," or the uniqueness of time, that
is at the center of the novel, and this is a theological and philosophical
question. To create, a novelist walks a curious tightrope—without
recurrence, there is no form; without uniqueness, characters have no
real meaning. (The Schulz story too is about time. There are many
paragraphs that speak to the complexity of time, its sadness, which
has allowed the sanatorium.) The question of time is what mediates
reality in fiction. And the complexity of fiction can almost always be
measured by two sticks—language, which is discernible only in the
original, and time, which is a universal and translates immediately. In
this sense, plot, as a creature of time, is the heart of the novel, but
only as the stepsister of time, never for its own sake.

Kundera's material fixe (I hesitate to say idée fixe), excrement or
evacuation, is treated humorously in the Talmud—obsession with it,
disgust, excitement, is not a preoccupation of the rabbis. Luther,
rather than Rabbi Akiba, makes it his medium. Kundera's assumption that there is no excitement without excrement seems rather
shaky. I heard a more interesting explanation, as far as my own sexual

life is concerned, from Rabbi Joseph Soloveitchik. While leaving moot the question of whether or not Adam and Eve had sex before leaving the garden, he spoke to the question of *chayt*, sin. It was the act of sin that revealed to Adam and Eve their shame. And this discovery was not a step backward, according to Rabbi Soloveitchik, but a step forward, for shame indicates the presence of a spiritual life. It is a sense of the ecstatic possibilities of sexual intercourse as a medium for mystical ascent that intrigued the rabbis, and that welled up in the literature of the kabala. Of course, the rabbis were not unique in their view—the poets of Provence, the writers of the "sweet new style" (Dante among them), with the language of Neoplatonism, saw love as a ladder that would bring them into ecstatic congress with the Unknown. For Dante, the garden, the physical garden of paradise, as such, is located rather low on the ascent toward the Unknown. He wished to go up to the stars for sexual experience.

Why does this handful of inherited stories obsess the West? For one, good or ill, they are our inheritance, bound up with our language. Ignoring them, we ignore the memory of our speech. It is always disturbing for a nationalist to discover that the oldest stories, ones that are the touchstones of childhood and of nations, were told before the nation existed, and that characteristic tales of the shape shifter, monkey-god, coyote, diminutive hero, and giant belong to dim antiquity. Yet there is a far distance between, say, *Oedipus Rex* and *Tom Jones*. Though both use the same story—a son is tricked into sleeping with his mother—the differences speak a great deal not only about the authors, but about their centuries and about the national audiences that listened to their stories. In *The Inferno*, Dante gives a tour of death that, despite all the baroque trappings of medieval Catholicism, remains gripping and frightening. Along with these, I found myself rereading the *Aeneid*, without which the bridge between Homer and Dante cannot be understood.

The attempt to create a new religious literature is one of our contemporary struggles. I feel it very strongly in Kafka, for instance, in *The Metamorphosis, Investigations of a Dog*, and *Josephine of the Mouse Folk*, for instance. It is not surprising that these were written by a man who was studying Hebrew and dreaming of emigration to Palestine.

Fiction requires perhaps a certain irrational attention to the past, to a language of analogue dancing like the bees in the air, but by syllable, and ear. Joyce came very close to writing a religious book with *Ulysses,* a sensitive reworking of the allegorical tradition in which Dante and many others read the adventures of Homer's hero. The attempt to write religious epic is, of course, fraught with dangers, principally of the ego. Joyce, I believe, broke down completely in *Finnegan's Wake* and lost a sense of human dimension, his connection with past structures of reading, and made himself unintelligible to all but the highly paid initiates of the academic profession, who celebrate him as mystery cult figure. Thoreau too abandoned himself to the minutiae of observation at the end, as if—like Borges's character Funes, in the story "Funes, the Memorious"—the present, with its startling omnivorous appetite for attention and suspension, broke in on the writer and so mesmerized him that he lost the connection of past and future.

Dante and Thoreau fascinate me as writers because of their attempts to write religious epic and to tell their own stories within it. Naturally, they are both solipsists, who see the universe revolve around them, and in that sense, like Job, they cling to the Hebrew cosmology, in which a human narrator can claim the attention of the Divine. This is a radical claim, for if the narrator can, so can the reader. The rights of individuals, men and women, to give themselves a central place in the drama of life and death, to conduct the trial—Kakfa's in *The Trial,* or Job's—is one of the presumptions of fiction.

Looking back now on the classics of twentieth-century fiction, I see a clear movement toward the personal, the idea of the writer, the narrator, as the most interesting imagination of the fiction, precisely because the sense of loneliness, of isolation, of fear, has grown so intolerable. It is impossible to write directly about the anxiety of death—death not only of the individual, but of the family; of religious belief; of society; of the planet, of human sexual possibility, given the biological threat of new or newly understood viruses. Nevertheless, this terrible noise is the background against which the I, the ego, the notion of the narrator, has to struggle, to make itself heard. The notion of a deliberate deception is what has shaped the most interesting contemporary narrative in fiction. It is the idea that

Thoreau, who had burned down a large tract in his own beloved
woods and remained fascinated with fire, entertained when he talked
about seeing a lie through to the truth; the idea of walking into the
local scrub and making it resonate as if it were the heart of the
American wilderness; the idea of the self-sufficient narrator, which
Defoe somehow so brilliantly stumbled on, finding the practical,
eccentric language that Shakespeare had been looking for in *The
Tempest.*

Take Frisch's *A Wilderness of Mirrors.* The narrator pretends to be
blind in order to see his wife commit adultery, to see his wife as he
could not see her if he were not blind. A like idea, the question of
murder and wish, makes Frisch's hero in *Man in the Holocene* wonder
whether or not he has killed his wife. The narrator cannot remember.
His murdering cannot be proved, only his dreams can indicate it.
This deception operates as well in Beckett's acid text *First Love,* where
a crabbed misogynist falls in love with a filthy bag lady on a Dublin
bench. Beckett manages to make us feel the necessity of the romantic
against all possible odds.

In fiction a handful of stories recur. Part of the sense of shape in
narrative is this recurrence. I always sound out a quotation from
Robert Creeley, who wrote only a few short stories but managed one of
the best definitions of their writing: "I begin where I can and end
when I see the whole thing returning." Again I come back to this
paradox of the unique and the repetitive in the same breath. It feeds
that sense of falling back, of the circular movement, of man, particular, but caught in a pattern. A certain breakdown in hierarchy is
valuable for the novel. The dimensions of the breakdown—as we are
experiencing now, unfortunately—are almost impossible to express.
The strength, for instance, of Latin American novels through the past
thirty years was that their hierarchies were still intact, and from the
vantage point of Paris, New York, or even the foreign newspapers,
they had a strange perspective on their slow decay. The Germans too
observed how much of their hierarchy had survived the devastation of
the war and was only slowly passing out of existence. So Faulkner and
James come at the end of traditions under a strain too great for them to
keep their form, and the novelist finds form for the tradition within

words. That is a valuable way of understanding what is happening, although it may be that genius is too individual to relate entirely to society. Without an audience, however, both of that society and outside it, there is no performance, no matter how brief the audience's attention. Someone had to listen to Henry James, appreciate his ear; look at William Faulkner's novels, respond to them. The growing isolation of the individual is seen often in the isolation of our best writers, as if it were a condition of their hearing the anxiety, the quiet without which the noise cannot be monitored.

This was the genius of Defoe, to discover not an uninhabited island, but the island on which man would be absolutely alone, outside of society, and somehow have to make a life. Not Defoe as journalist but Defoe as dreamer has come to dominate fiction—Defoe as defined by his own narrator, Robinson Crusoe, who created a life of his own in literature, after his creator had died. Kafka, in fact, sees himself as Crusoe, in one of his letters to Milena.

Robinson you see, had to sign on, make the dangerous voyage, had to suffer shipwreck and many other things—I would only have to lose you and already I'd be Robinson. But I would be more Robinson than he. He still had the Island and Friday, and many things and finally the ship which took him off and almost turned everything into a dream again—I would have nothing, not even a name, this too I gave to you.

And this is why I, in a sense, am independent of you, just because the dependency reaches beyond all bounds. The either/or is too great. Either you are mine, in which case it's good, or I lose you, in which case it's not just bad but simply nothing. In that case there wouldn't be any jealousy, no suffering, no anxiety—nothing. And there's certainly something blasphemous about building so much on one person, and this is also the reason why fear creeps round the foundations. It's not, however, so much the fear about you as the fear about daring to build like this at all. And this is why in self-defense (but it has probably always been so) so many divine qualities mingle with the human ones in your dear face.

So now Samson has told Delilah his secret and she can cut off his hair which she has always been ruffling in anticipation—but let her! As long as she hasn't a similar secret, nothing else matters. [5]

Similarly, Cervantes discovered that his narrator Cide Hamete, an Arab (according to some commentators, a Moroccan Jew), had assumed a life of his own. Hamete gave voice to the stifled cry of Spain before the expulsions and satirized the notion of Christian knighthood. Not only Don Quixote's distortions but the joke of the narrator of these distortions slowly turns so serious that the comedy becomes the tragedy of a nation that has lost all sense of redeeming illusions.

I read Defoe and Cervantes in the mirror of Kafka, who wrote: "I think we ought to read only the kind of books that wound and stab us. If the book we're reading doesn't wake us up with a blow on the head, what are we reading it for? So that it will make us happy, as you write? Good Lord, we would be happy precisely if we had no books, and the kind of books that make us happy are the kind we could write ourselves if we had to. But we need the books that affect us like a disaster, that grieve us deeply, like the death of someone we loved more than ourselves, like being banished into forests far from everyone, like a suicide. A book must be the axe for the frozen sea inside us. That is my belief."[6]

And again, a quotation: "This anxiety, this terrible anxiety, which will not cease until the book of Genesis is rescinded." For fiction is not only the record but the source of anxiety—and so in that fearful story of Borges, *Tlon, Uqber, Orbis Tertius,* a spurious encyclopedia slowly changes the reality of the world, as men's ideas of a perfect society set society off on a murderous construction of reality, "a labyrinth devised by men, a labyrinth destined to be deciphered by men."

Dante went to an island full of spirits, purgatory, though his frustration at their bodilessness brought him over and over to the brink of despair as he reached out, rising higher, hoping to touch the dead Beatrice. Thoreau went to the woods as to an island, dreaming that the trees would bend toward him and give him an erotic life. Robinson Crusoe found an empty island where the adventures he sought came to him—the lust of cannibals, the perfect service of a savage he could train to be son, mate, and society.

To be gripped by these fictions, even while acknowledging that they are fictions, is to live them, and to wander in a sense in one's dreams. To live without them is often to live a life so bleak as to be unendurable. Kundera found that Marxism had largely degenerated into kitsch. Borges felt that an idealism without angels had created a human ruthlessness more dangerous than any hitherto known. The rabbis were aware, for instance, that much of Genesis was a fiction, a fable; but that did not release them from the obligation to read and be inspired by it, for they felt the same uncanny workings of the Unknown in their unconscious as they read and dreamed the fable over.

The novel of social realism, to which the new journalists inevitably migrated, has no such music in its air, nor are there any answers or, more important, questions about the conditions of life at the edge. There is no view into the life to come or, for that matter, the life that is irremediably past. Too often the obvious amusement that accompanies this so-called new novel, its parody of social manner, is really reassurance to the audience. The world of man's stupidity, inhumanity, and can't can be laughed at; therefore it can be put down, delimited, understood. *Pedro Paramo,* the stunning novel of social horror by Mexican writer Juan Rulfo, takes place in a world so deprived that the living do not know who among them is alive and who is already dead. This speaks to a reality that has become insane. Its language is not the coy, clever lip of those social realists, whose heroes and villains remain caricatures, but the voice of shock, dread.

The journalist always remains outside his subject, unwilling to undergo self-examination. He is the entertainer, reporter, despite the pretensions of moral judgment. The novelist is driven to confession and its fictional art forms, dream, romance, idyll. And here—even in Eden or at the lost horizon in the sea, a true encounter will leave one naked and howling.

NOTES

[1] Tom Wolfe, "Why They Aren't Writing the Great American Novel Anymore," *Esquire,* December 1972, p. 274.

[2] Mark Jay Mirsky, *The Secret Table* (New York: Fiction Collective/Braziller, 1975), p. 59.

3 Franz Kafka, *Letters to Milena,* trans. Tania and James Stern (New York: Schocken, 1962), p. 178.

4 Milan Kundera, *The Unbearable Lightness of Being* (New York: Harper & Row, 1985), pp. 246–247

5 Kafka, op. cit., pp. 194–195.

6 Kafka, letter to Oskar Pollak, January 27, 1904.

The Body of History

MORRIS BERMAN

Western history, Western philosophy, and even Western anthropology have developed with little or no reference to the human body. Somehow, Western academic understanding tacitly assumes that the human body has nothing to tell us, has no knowledge or "information"; that for all practical purposes, it isn't even there.

What if it turned out that most of what was in the history books, or even in the daily newspapers, had nothing to do with life as it was actually lived? This seems a most curious suggestion; after all, what could all that stuff that fills much of the world's libraries be about, if not "the human story"? And yet I do not believe this suggestion is as strange as it sounds. Let us explore this possibility, just for a moment.

I was born and raised in upstate New York. During my high school years, we were required, as part of the history sequence of our education, to spend time learning about local and regional history. Our textbook had a chapter about the Colonial period, another about the defeat of the Iroquois, still another about the building of the Erie Canal, as well as ones on the rise of the steel and textile industries. For all I remember, there may even have been chapters on working-class movements, strikes, the formation of labor unions, possibly something on the life of Emma Goldman (though I doubt it).

That I *don't* remember is largely the point here. It was all crushingly boring; it seemed to have little relevance to anything that really mattered, to me or any of the other students forced to study this material. Yet it never occurred to me that there was anything wrong with this, because *all* of high school—or, I should say, the part devoted to formal education—was boring. Chemistry and Latin were no different from history, even though history was supposedly about "real life." Yet none of us were deceived about what actually constituted real life. Real life was your awkwardness in front of the opposite sex, your relations with your peers, your struggle to cope with what went on in your family. And for many of us, fear played a large part in all of these dramas. Yet none of this was in the history books; why (white) people bothered killing Native Americans or building canals remained a total mystery, and not a very interesting one at that. History, no less than chemistry or Latin, was a set of abstractions, a bunch of formulas to be learned and later repeated. Which is what we did.

It will, of course, be argued that all of high school is a disaster, generally for everyone, and that my use of textbooks written for teenagers is an unfair example. But is it really? Pick up almost any history monograph today, including ones written by sophisticated or "sympathetic" historians, and you will generally confront the problem of reading about things that somehow fail to resonate with what is most familiar to you. And what is that? In a word, your emotions. Your emotions are what your real life is about; they reflect the things that matter the most to you. The human drama is first and foremost an emotional one. How is it, then, that emotions—which is to say, the life of the body, which is where the emotions are felt—get left out of academic history? And if that is the case, what can such a history possibly tell us about the past?

Of course, much has changed since I had to learn about the construction of the Erie Canal. Since 1965 in particular, there has been a conscious attempt in academic circles to effect a marriage of the abstract and the concrete by means of interdisciplinary work in history and social anthropology. Social anthropology operates on an intimate level; it studies face-to-face and day-to-day interactions of individuals in particular communities. [1] But until recently, it made no attempt to fit this material into a coherent whole or extrapolate it backward into the past; and historians never saw this material as having any value for their own discipline. In the last twenty or so years, however, there have been important efforts in these directions. British and French historians in particular have attempted to use the "stuff of daily life" to create long-range studies (covering three or four centuries) of things such as family relations, religious movements, and the practice and persecution of witchcraft. In addition, the study of *mentalité,* as it is called, has done much to probe the nonrational foundations of human history (more on this below). Yet in all this work, and even in the work of the social anthropologists, there remains a failure of resonance. Anthropologists, for example, will talk in terms of rights and obligations within kinship groups, but words such as *love* and *hate* never surface in their analyses. [2] The life of the body, the life of our emotions, remains mysterious, unpredictable. Thus, although I find many of the developments in historiography since 1965 intellectually fascinating, I am convinced that the major historiographical revolution is yet to come. Western history, Western philosophy, and even Western anthropology have developed with little or no reference to the human body. Somehow, Western academic understanding tacitly assumes that the human body has nothing to tell us, has no knowledge or "information"; that for all practical purposes, it isn't even there. And yet the life of the body is our real life, the only life we have.

Contrasts with "nonliterate" civilizations can be very instructive on this point. I put the word in quotes because our own civilization equates literacy with literature, with the printed text; it does not *consciously* understand that there is such a thing as body literacy (on an unconscious level, though, it understands this very well). Some time ago, I saw the premiere of a dance concert called "Rainforest," performed by a Vancouver group called the Karen Jamieson Dance Company. The choreography was so raw that I often felt I had stuck my finger into an electric socket. The vignettes in this work are taken from the life of the Northwest Indians, principally the Haida, and they weave a cosmology that is entirely body-based. Gesture and grimace, blood and sexuality, darkness and light, tumble out in a shifting kaleidoscope, stunning the audience relentlessly with what they already know: This is your real life, no matter what else you pretend. The director, Karen Jamieson, performs two of the vignettes by herself: one of a tour guide pointing to satellite maps of the earth and saying, "You are here," the other of a "correctly" dressed anthropologist with a microphone narrating a museum survey of Indian artifacts. In the latter, the anthropologist loses her grounding as the cord from the mike gets coiled around her ankles; and the implication of the tour guide's "You are here," in contrast with the Haida, who are *truly* present on the earth, is obvious. "You are nowhere" with this mode of rootless, disembodied analysis; to leave your body and believe you can still know anything at all is quite literally a form of madness. The boredom of our schools testifies to the fact that none of us are fooled by this charade.

Regardless of what people visibly present to the world, they have a secret life, one that is grounded in their emotions, their bodily relationship to the world and to themselves. History has failed to tell us about these things, because as a discipline it moves along the lines of external description. The academic study of human life, despite the various efforts in the field of psychohistory (work that is very often highly formulistic), proceeds on the assumption that only the visible is real. The reason this work is finally empty is that from a certain vantage point, it all amounts to the same book, written over and over again, but in different guises. Academic discourses generally lack the power to shock, to move the reader—which is to say, they lack the power to teach. They fail to address the felt, visceral level of our being, and so possess an air of unreality.

History is written with the mind holding the pen. What would it look like, what would it read like, if it were written with the *body* holding the pen? I suspect it would be a very different story, one that would revolve around the hidden, somatic roots of our more visible behavior. Such a history would open us to our own emotional life; it would lead us into a world of visceral identification, tangible resonance. It would read like a good novel, but it would not be invented. This "subjective" experience is "what actually happened"; writing about the past in this way would be "objective" in the truest sense of the word. At present, however, no historian, myself included, has really explored this possibility to any great extent, though several have made promising beginnings—Carlo Ginzburg, Norbert Elias, and Theodore Zeldin, among others (discussed below). And in almost all these cases, the historian has recognized that he has come up against a methodological wall; that the possibility of a new, emergent type of history requires the simultaneous emergence of new criteria for assessing what happened in the past. Opening the door on a new world requires a completely new set of procedures for negotiating the threshold; it has always been this way. Hence we find a growing number of historians arguing that the epistemological, or "scientific," dimensions of the discipline itself are too confining, and that the notion of objectivity as it has evolved over the last few centuries actually works against true understanding. But (as always) the obstacles to pushing into this new territory are formidable. Before we can imagine what a somatic, or visceral, history would consist of, it might be useful to understand what some of these obstacles are.

⊏═══⊐

The major obstacle to understanding the past in the way I am suggesting is, curiously enough, the problem of living in the modern period itself—that is, during the time in which history became a professional discipline, modeled along the lines of the natural sciences. Previously, history was by and large a mode of storytelling. This is not to say that it was "merely" (note how loaded our terms are) fiction, though its concern with "the facts" was certainly far less than our own. It would be more accurate to say that it had a very different sense of what the facts were. In this mode, the facts were first and foremost what happened on a psychic and emotional level; indeed, if this got left out, it was fair to say that *nothing happened*—there was no story to tell. The essential truth was an interior one; to omit this was to give the reader, or listener, no significant information whatsoever. In the transition to modernity, this emphasis on interior knowing was severely attenuated.

When I say "modern period," I am talking about the stretch of time from the Scientific Revolution—say, the mid-sixteenth century—to the present. A whole series of disciplines has grown and flourished over the last four hundred years. Alchemy gave way to chemistry, astrology to astronomy, mythology to psychoanalysis, and, as noted, storytelling to professional, academic history. Most of us would agree that this shift represents an increase in our mode of understanding the natural and social world—specifically, a gain in what we call "objectivity." And the essential feature of this mode of understanding is that of psychic distance, the existence of a rigid barrier between observer and observed. If you become emotional about a subject you are analyzing, if you do experience identification or resonance, you disqualify yourself as a professional observer or analyst. "Emotional" in the modern period has the same force as "unreliable"; it means you are biased, that your judgment cannot be counted on. I suspect most of us would agree with this; I am trying to suggest only that our agreement is part of a culturally conditioned process. Prior to 1600, *lack* of identification was regarded as strange. Perception and cognition emerged primarily from the body, which is why, to borrow a term from the anthropologists, everything possessed *mana,* was alive. In this sense, it is difficult to imagine how profoundly different, almost totally disparate, oral and written cultures are. The former had a somatic base so solid that their reality was totally different from our own.

An interesting discussion of somatic versus oral culture is provided by Eric Havelock in his book *Preface to Plato,* in which he describes the mode of education in pre-Homeric Greece. Havelock writes that mimesis, or active emotional identification with a speaker or chorus, was the way in which the knowledge of the culture was passed on. This knowledge, in the form of poetry, was recited before a large audience that memorized the verses in a state of autohypnosis. Mimesis, the root of our words *mime* and *mimicry,* was the submission to the spell of the performer and was a process with physiological effects that were at once relaxing and erotic. Learning went on at the level of the body. Knowledge was, in consequence, directly experiential; there was no (or little) separate intellectual analysis that commented on the world or regarded it from a distance. [3]

A similar mode of understanding prevailed during much of the Middle Ages. This form of participating consciousness, as it has been called, was very likely not so pure as that of pre-Homeric Greece, but it existed nonetheless. A host of crafts and disciplines had an absorbing, repetitive, trancelike aspect and were highly mesmerizing and sensuous. This was especially true of the occult sciences, such as alchemy and witchcraft; Thomas Goldstein, the medieval historian, makes the same point about cathedral building. [4] In all these cases, the route to true understanding was to be found in that absorption, in the loss of psychic distance. Participation, or identification, is highly sensuous in nature, and it is a mode of knowing that cannot be intellectually refuted because of its immediate, visceral quality.

It can, however, be intellectually *rejected,* or intellectually repressed, which was what much of the Scientific Revolution was about. Yet if the truth be told, it is not that our emotional life was repressed, but that one particular emotion triumphed above all the rest. "Emotionless" activity, such as scientific or academic detachment, is driven by a very definite emotion, namely, the craving for psychological and existential security.[5] The increasing preoccupation with psychic distance can be seen in most areas of human activity from the Renaissance on. In art we have the discovery of perspective, a device that assumes a neutral spectator looking at the painting from the outside, at a distance. The shift from alchemy to chemistry, and what that symbolized, meant that emotional identification was also abandoned in favor of psychic distance. Similarly, a good astrologer must know how to feel a situation out emotionally; a good astronomer, on the other hand, takes care not to let emotions influence observations (and is generally unaware that detachment is an emotion).

This shift took a long time, and it represented an increasing "masculinization" of culture and consciousness. Physics was affected first, then chemistry, biology, and finally the study of human life. By the middle of the eighteenth century the work of Isaac Newton had become the model for the social sciences, and in the nineteenth century, Comtean positivism affected history and sociology alike. Psychology in its turn was seen as a branch of biology, itself conceived of as a subdivision of physics.

The heavy professionalization of history began in the nineteenth century. Leopold von Ranke, the noted German historian, set the tone for historical research by asserting that the job of the historian was nothing more or less than to give a straight account of the facts, to report "what actually occurred." Despite a few deviations from this theme, it is a goal most historians still share, and it has at its core the notion of psychic distance, of a past "out there" that is somehow, miraculously, independent of our interpretations of it. Interpretation of the facts is, of course, necessary, but this is not really seen as changing the "hard bedrock of reality." Emotional identification with the facts, however, is totally out of the question; it smacks of participating consciousness, and is to be avoided at all costs. The triumph of the Scientific Revolution in the realm of historical understanding meant that things must never be examined except from the outside. And this, *mutatis mutandis,* is where we still are today. The body and its feelings have no apparent relationship to the historical process; the "inside" simply doesn't count. History is, quite literally, a superficial discipline.[6]

The result of all this is that a lot of historical analysis today is simultaneously orthodox in methodology and unbelievable in content. I could easily turn this essay into a review article of such works, but let me instead cite one or two examples from my own experience.

Some years ago I had a colleague who was studying eighteenth-century German Pietism and was collecting data on how many people went to church in some small village in Hesse or Baden (the exact location slips my mind) over a period of several decades. Attendance, according to the parish register, was very high, and my colleague used this to argue for a high degree of religious sentiment in that region. I voiced my doubts as to whether the two things were necessarily related. That is, statistics are fine, but the German villagers in question may have been in church for other reasons besides God. The real objectivity here, if any sort of *Geistesgeschichte* were being attempted, had to be intensely subjective—that is, had to focus on the inner life. Well, as this sort of information is methodologically invisible to traditional historical analysis, my colleague regarded my question as meaningless. I, in turn, regarded the methodology itself as meaningless or, at the very least, seriously misapplied, and there is no way I know to resolve this conflict.

A similar incident occurred with another colleague, who was doing a computer analysis of medieval saints. The project, which had no trouble attracting grant support, struck me as fundamentally wacky. His method was to compile all kinds of data on these religious figures—social class, country of origin, age at which they had their major ecstatic experience (if they had one at all)—and run the information through a computer. It was as though he somehow hoped to compute the cubic volume of the soul, to distill the essence of mystical experience and yet manage to escape the direct loss of consciousness that makes the experience meaningful at all (because ineffable). The project seemed stereotypical, a classic product of what one of my friends calls "the age of quantitative mysticism." When I suggested to my colleague that he might possibly learn more about sainthood from thirty seconds of religious ecstasy than three-hundred hours of FORTRAN time, he effectively told me that I must be crazy. Yet where does sanity lie in all this? That is indeed the crux of the matter. Who knows more about medieval sainthood—the historian who compiles data on age and nationality or the one who goes to a monastery and sits in a cell for several months in complete silence? What does it mean, "to know," anyway? Again, there is a conflict of viewpoint here that is completely unresolvable.

The whole problem of inside versus outside, and its consequences for knowing, was raised some time ago by Lewis Mumford in a critique of academic studies of archaic civilization. Mumford attacked the notion, promoted in particular by the discipline of archaeology, that man was first and foremost a tool user—*Homo faber*. That archaeologists drew this conclusion is no surprise, Mumford said, given that the artifacts of their discipline are by and large material items that do not perish easily, such as stone hammers and flint arrowheads. But, he went on, suppose some ancient culture had a fantastic mode of conflict resolution or a brilliant technique of dream analysis? What if it were the case—and Mumford believed this—that archaic human expression came through the body, in activities such as mime, dance, song, and ritual, as well as symbolically, via gesture or cave painting? By the very nature of these activities, no artifacts would be left; in fact, when the first cave paintings were discovered in Spain in 1879, anthropologists denounced them as a hoax. This emphasis on "hard data," from the viewpoint of common sense, makes no sense at all. As Mumford put it, "This apparently solid evidence is full of holes." "Material artifacts may stubbornly defy time," he wrote, "but what they tell about man's history is a good deal less than the truth." Contemporary Australian bushpeople, for example, have a very rudimentary technology but very complex religious ceremonies, kinship organization, and language. Future archaeologists caught up in the *Homo faber* model will inevitably dismiss them as a nonculture, as we have done with archaic man and woman. Yet it is precisely these somatic and symbolic activities that very likely constituted the major part of the life of archaic humans. These are the things that were most representative of their value system, the things in which they invested most of their energy. But as Mumford noted, these essential, "interior" activities are invisible to traditional academic analysis.[7]

A similar situation can be found in the field of evolutionary biology. Certain hard-shelled animals—crustaceans such as the horseshoe crab, for example—have an extremely tough exoskeleton, and it is this shell that, deposited in mud and rock, forms the visible record of the creatures' evolution. Allowing for what Darwin called "imperfections in the geological record," these fossils enable the biologist to draw a fairly neat evolutionary picture. The problem is that the exoskeleton is essentially the defense system of these animals; eyes, digestive apparatus, and nervous system are contained within the soft, gushy interior, the part that rapidly decomposes upon death. This gushy interior is *not* preserved in the fossil record. Paleontological reconstructions based on the exoskeleton are very similar to archaeological reconstructions based on arrowheads and implements of war. Thus it becomes very easy to conclude that the essential activity of the horseshoe crab or human being is attack and defense. But this is *not* the exclusive or essential activity of either organism; for both, the larger part of life goes on inside the gushy interior. Darwin anticipated Mumford, in a way, when he wrote: "No organism wholly soft can be preserved."[8] Organisms or cultures that are partially soft can very easily fool the biologist, the archaeologist, and the historian. Which approach, then, should we trust—a "hard-nosed" methodology that is blind to what is essential or a commonsense evaluation that points to what is being left out?

"On the surface, an intelligible lie," says one of Milan Kundera's characters in *The Unbearable Lightness of Being;* "underneath, the unintelligible truth." Certainly, if these are our only choices, we might as well forget the whole thing right now. If we want the historical truth, we are going to have to set aside our obsession with objectivity and its attendant methodologies and come up with a completely different approach, one that can reliably take us into the center of the gushy interior. And what we find there are those topics tied up with the body, the emotions, and inner psychic perception: religious experience, love and sexuality, humor, anger, insults, play and fantasy, sound (not the history of music, which is a very different thing), boredom, depression, fun, crying, sneezing, gesture, the treatment of body hair, anxiety, addiction, suicide, creativity (not simply the history of art), Oedipal tensions, incest, and so on. The Chilean biologist Francisco Varela once remarked that the hard sciences deal with the soft questions and the soft sciences deal with the hard ones. What I am calling for is a new type of historical "science" that can deal with the hard—that is to say, truly significant—issues of human life. For such a methodology, studying religious feeling through parish records, or ecstatic experience through computer correlations, would be completely softheaded.

An interesting discussion of what I am talking about is provided by the British psychiatrist R. D. Laing in his classic work, *The Divided Self.*[9] Pointing out that in the English language the word *merely* never precedes the word *objective,* Laing goes on to give the example of Alfred Kinsey, the pioneering sexologist who spent his life gathering information on American sexual behavior. Through surveys, questionnaires, and interviews, Kindsey painstakingly compiled data on (among other things) the frequency of intercourse among married couples. But let us assume that he wanted to be even *more* objective, *absolutely* certain of his data. Imagine, then, Alfred Kinsey tiptoeing across suburban lawns every evening, peering into windows and recording the incidence of sexual activity, until finally he could produce the "hard" statistics he was looking for—for example, "the American middle-class couple engages in intercourse an average of 3.4 times per week."

The scene then shifts to Laing's consulting room, where a patient is explaining to the doctor that for years he hasn't "really" been having sex with his wife. Yes, penis has gone into vagina an average of 3.4 (or whatever) times per week, but during this act the patient has been disconnected from the activity and has mentally been floating on the ceiling watching the activity go on. He has, in fact, been observing his wife having sex with his *imago,* or detached bodily image, and observing her thinking that she is engaged in intercourse with him. But he (at this point Laing begins to underline the word *he*) knows better.

Now who is *he*? Has this man *really* been making love to his wife all these years? If the answer is yes, then what's the problem? Why is he consulting a psychiatrist? For surely, his activity satisfies all the tests for reality that objective, nonparticipating scientific analysis requires. And this is precisely the problem: Kinsey was dealing with *merely objective evidence;* his data tell us nothing about American sexuality. And the reason for this is that sexuality is part of the gushy interior; the crux of it is where the mind is in relation to the body, as anyone who has ever made love knows. Wiring people up à la Masters and Johnson could happen only in an age caught in the grip of quantitative mysticism.

It now becomes clear why I was bored in high school—and why you probably were as well (at least in class). Historical objectivity is not merely boring; it is also, quite simply, wrong. And on some level, the body knows this. This is why we found it difficult even to sit still in school. That restlessness is the body's way of flashing us an essential message: "This is bullshit," the body is saying; "don't listen to this." Pick up a recent copy of virtually any academic history journal (add sociology, psychology, etc., etc.), and the chances are good that your body will have the same reaction it did in high school.

I once heard the American poet Robert Bly read one of his poems and admit that he didn't know what the concluding line meant. But, he added, he knew that the line belonged there, because as he wrote it, he felt a twinge in his gut. Of course, history is not poetry, and I very much doubt that "gut twingeing" can serve as an adequate methodology for historians. But to be honest, I don't think it's a bad start. History is *made* somatically; to be accurate, then, it should be *written* somatically. If a twinge doesn't add up to a methodology, it can at least be an indicator of inner accuracy, which is, I think, the point Bly was trying to make.

There are two modes of reportage about the past I know of that produce the kind of twinge Bly was talking about. One is mythology, specifically, fairy tales; the other is historical fiction, at least some of it. I am not suggesting that history be converted into fairy tales or fiction; that is too easy a way out, or so it seems to me. But I want to dwell on these for a moment because as indicators, they do point in the direction of a deeper understanding of the human condition.

The problems I have been wrestling with up to this point can be made very palpable by attending the meetings of a learned society, where people stand up and read papers, and then attending a session of storytelling, especially when the latter deals with myths or fairy tales. Historians typically say to each other at the conclusion of a professional conference (usually sotto voce) that they learned more chatting over coffee than they did from the formal sessions, and they laugh. There is nothing surprising about this; the laughter is understandable. For we are bodies as well as minds, and the formal sessions tend to deal with topics, and to deal with them in such a way, that the body is left out. By contrast, at storytelling conferences (and these are growing increasingly popular) the body and its concomitant emotions are immediately engaged, along with the mind. So deep does this material cut that an audience can typically be found howling with laughter or in a state of panic. It is not that the mind is left out here; it's just that it is not examining things strictly from the outside. Storytellers make an assumption that historians rarely do: that human beings are *not* rational; that they cannot be understood in terms of objective analysis; and that their deepest and most significant experiences are lived on a level that is largely invisible, a shadowy region where the mind and the body move in and out of each other in an infinite number of elusive combinations, and that can be evoked only through allusion, feeling tone, rhetoric, and "resonance." And these storytelling conferences also assume what academic history must by definition deny: that this shadow world is what human life is really about and is the crucible in which history, in the final analysis, is really made.

As for fiction, how shall we study, let us say, the Russian revolution of 1905, or the German occupation of Rome? There have been numerous analyses of both these events. In the case of the former, for example, we learn about wage-price spirals in the closing years of the nineteenth century, the social backgrounds of revolutionary groups, military skirmishes, ideological debates, and the effectiveness of the czar's army in squelching the revolt. Footnotes refer us to newspapers, subversive tracts, economic indices, police reports, letters and correspondence of relevant individuals. All of this is well and good; it is

certainly "real," in that it refers to events that actually occurred, as
Ranke said. Yet I never had any sense of the 1905 revolution until I
read Andrei Bely's novel *Petersburg,* which zeroes in on the generational conflict between a father, who is highly placed in the czarist
bureaucracy, and his son, who inadvertently gets caught up in the
revolutionary movement. As events move toward their climax, Bely
presents us with a surreal dream sequence, in which the son experiences his mind separated from his body, floating through the cosmos.
As the narrative proceeded from that point, I began to feel the twinge
Bly spoke of. In fact, I was mesmerized; my own critical faculties were
suspended as my body started to go through a mild anxiety reaction
and somehow entered into the events of 1905. It is easy to say that this
is simply a testimony to Bely's literary talents, and that the whole
thing is an excellent imaginative reconstruction. But anyone who
knows about anxiety reactions—and all of our bodies know it, and
know it well—recognizes that if this did not actually take place as
Bely describes it, then *something* like it must have, because this surreal
"onlooker" experience is always triggered when your moorings come
undone or when you come face-to-face with impending psychic death.
Revolution is not a rational event; it cannot be grasped or even
"explained" in terms of ideological debates or wage-price spirals. In
fact, many years ago I heard the British historian Eric Hobsbawm—a
student of revolution if there ever was one—give a lecture at the
London School of Economics in which he candidly admitted that he
had no idea why revolutions occurred, and that as far as he could make
out, they were large-scale "happenings." Bely, quite simply, captured
an essential component of what goes on during such a happening.[10]

A second example is afforded by Elsa Morante's *La Storia* (History).
The novel, which is about the German occupation of Rome, revolves
around the rounding up of the city's Jews on October 16, 1943. The
central character, a schoolteacher named Ida Mancuso, happens to
stumble upon the Tiburtino railway station more or less by accident
during the event. The scene is one of cattle cars and chaos, and at the
level of immediate perception, Ida has no idea of what is going on. For
months a demented woman has been wandering around the Jewish
ghetto (where Ida occasionally does her shopping) hysterically pro-

claiming that the Jews would be shipped off and destroyed. Ida's infant son, Useppe, whom she holds in her arms as she stands on the platform, suddenly turns to her and stares into her eyes with a look of questioning horror. Months later Ida returns to the now abandoned station, wanders into one of the nearby apartments, its windows broken, the corners of the rooms filled with cobwebs, and sits down. Suddenly, involuntarily, the words escape from her body, as it were: "They're all dead," she says aloud, allowing herself finally to acknowledge verbally what she knew viscerally on October 16. It is a tour de force, this moment; I felt my whole body quivering, on the edge of tears and immense grief. Again, it is no use claiming that this is merely a question of literary power. It *is*; but whether Ida actually existed or not is much beside the point. Morante cites a number of historical studies of the fate of the Italian Jews in her bibliography, but she has captured something that they, I suspect, have not: Evil has something to do with somatic disturbance, and the recognition of evil has something to do with somatic awareness. It is not for nothing that she called her book *History*. This is *la storia*—the real story.[11]

Again, I am not suggesting that academic history departments be absorbed into those of creative writing, or that the American Historical Association devote its annual meeting to fairy tales. It might be an improvement of sorts, but I don't think that the cure for scientism is complete subjectivity. That would be merely the perpetuation of the mind-body dichotomy in a different form. But I do think these examples may help us on our way. By dealing directly with the nonrational, with the body, they give us a glimpse of what a *truly* objective historical reconstruction might necessarily include.

There is a small group of academic historians who have struggled with the role of the nonrational in human history, an offshoot of the so-called French *Annales* school whose writings date from the 1920s, though this offshoot includes two of the *Annales* founders, Lucien Febvre and Marc Bloch.[12] More recent exponents, such as Emmanuel LeRoy Ladurie and the Italian historian Carlo Ginzburg, have followed in the tradition of Febvre and Bloch, focusing their attention on subjects such as heresy, sorcery, peasant and popular culture, and in general the mindscape of the late Middle Ages. Febvre's pioneering study was of the problem of religious belief (actually, unbelief) in the sixteenth century; Bloch first set out to explore the cultural and symbolic significance of the medieval belief that the king's touch could heal scrofula. [13] In focusing on what Febvre called the "collective mental baggage" of a civilization, these historians moved far beyond what had passed, up to that point, for the mental life of a culture. They were not interested in intellectual history as such, but in *fundamental* outlooks—ones that reached, like a geological formation, far below the visible level. This was not, then, the history of ideas, but the history of psychic life in general, what they chose to call *mentalité*. I should add that this was not the same thing as psychohistory—that is, psychoanalysis applied to history. Febvre, Bloch, and others did not reduce the nonrational to the strictly sexual and did not approach their subjects with an a priori theoretical structure, Freudian or otherwise. Furthermore, they focused on entire cultures and civilizations rather than on single, significant individuals (as psychohistorians tend to do). [14]

The implications of this were at least twofold. First, such investigations tended to break down the distinction between "high" and "low" culture, even to suggest that what went on in the minds of ordinary people in any age was more significant, historically, than what went on in the minds of leading intellectuals or literary figures. Second, their work began to reveal (or suggest) the presence of serious mental discontinuities between successive periods of history. In mapping the psychic contours of the sixteenth century, for example, Febvre and Bloch were able to demonstrate the existence of a kind of mental watershed between the medieval and modern worlds. "Sacred" and "secular" are not just convenient intellectual categories; they are lived experiences, and neither can be understood from the outside. Living in a world where a person's touch was believed to be able to (could?) cure a specific disease is a very different psychic experience from living in a world where such things are regarded as impossible (and, perhaps as a result, do not occur).

All of this enlarged the possibilities for historical understanding quite dramatically, and in recent years, vast territories of invisible history—"unintelligible truth"—have started to emerge into view.

Most notable in this regard are Michel Foucault, who dealt with madness, sexuality, and the experience of punishment, and Philippe Ariès, who focused on childhood and death.[15] In *Les Mots et les choses* (Words and Things, translated into English as *The Order of Things*), Foucault took as his subject matter the nature of cognition itself, showing how as a code, or "mode of discourse," through which the world was perceived, premodern cognition was based on symbol and analogy, so that the world reflected itself in terms of feeling tone and resonance. It was Don Quixote's world, in which windmills could reasonably be giants, and in which walnuts, which resembled the brain in appearance, were in some sense small cerebrums and eaten as "brain food." For Foucault, writes the American historian Patrick Hutton, these modes of discourse "are the verbal expression of the mental structures (the 'words and things') through which man organizes his activities and classifies his perceptions of the world."[16] And again, the discourse of modernity is radically different from that of the sacred, medieval world: we are talking about two discontinuous orders of reality. Work of this sort finally opened the possibility of moving across this watershed, of recapturing past experience in the sense that it was actually lived, rather than through the filter of the post-sixteenth-century mode of discourse.

And yet, this did not happen. Foucault denied the possibility of crossing the watershed precisely *because* the forms of discourse were radically incommensurate, which meant, of course, that he was unable or unwilling to suspend his own consciousness. And this is the problem with virtually all studies in the field of *mentalité*: they stop short of the attempt to re-create a previous consciousness and opt instead for describing it from the vantage point of our own conceptual categories. In the last analysis, *mentalité* remains abstract, preserving the psychic distance so central to modern cognition. Mind and body, fact and value, still wind up on opposite sides of the fence. The history of mentalities reflects the great divide set up by the Scientific Revolution, and it in fact understands this. To remedy the situation, however, it goes on a journey that is ultimately baroque and convoluted. In this sense, the field of *mentalité* does have some similarities to Freudian psychoanalysis and a good bit of psychohistory.

That is to say, it attempts to recover the body by making a journey within the mind. In *Laws of Form,* Cambridge mathematician G. Spencer Brown—whose intellectual ancestry includes Lewis Carroll—pegs this exactly. The mind, he says, semideliberately cuts itself off from what it knows and then goes on an elaborate circular voyage to find it. [17] As Freud said, we know and we don't know, and we play this game of hide-and-seek all our lives (as Freud himself did). This peekaboo structure—itself a variant on the theme of psychic distance—has finally emerged as the real structure of modern cognition, and so long as the subjective experience of the body and the emotional life is excluded from historical understanding, we shall continue to go around in circles. Not that this is necessarily bad; at least, it seems to me that not all circles are vicious. But we do have to ask what lies outside the circle, what it would be like to step outside of it and into something else.

We come, then, to a boundary, and one that has a curious irony, or paradox, attached to it. In order to cross over to the premodern period, we have to abandon modern consciousness, at least temporarily; and this means we must abandon a certain type of egoic personality structure, allowing the mind to sink into the body, as it were. But that merger *is* premodern consciousness, or at least a good part of it. To explicate past consciousness, we must *become* it; and if we are terrified of doing that, we are condemned to move in an endless circle, our discourse finally beginning to resemble that of deaf-mutes discussing harmony, as Somerset Maugham once put it. It has been the fate of the history of mentalities, as historiography's cutting edge, to take us right up to the limits of traditional historical analysis and throw it into question. It is clear that psychic distance must now be abandoned as the criterion of truth, and that other criteria must be put in its place. This is the inevitable direction to go in; there are no other alternatives. But it is most unclear how to do this. The question of *Quo vadis* is inextricably linked with the question of how you will get there.

In the remaining pages of this discussion I shall make some suggestions that will undoubtedly strike professional historians (among others) as very much beyond the pale. But I wish to repeat what I stated earlier, that already a number of historians have commented on the nature of the crossroads at which we have finally arrived and the enormity of the problem involved in this transition. To take just one example, this whole methodological conundrum surfaced recently in the footnotes of a book on sixteenth-century heresy, *The Cheese and the Worms,* by Carlo Ginzburg. Ginzburg begins the book with an epigraph taken from the French author Louis Ferdinand Céline: "Everything that is interesting happens in the shadows; we know nothing of the real life of the human race." Searching in the shadows is both the major theme and the methodological undercurrent of the story that Ginzburg skillfully unfolds for us, that of Domenico Scandella, a peasant who was burned at the stake in 1599. Concerning Scandella, or Menocchio, as he was called, we learn two important facts: that his heretical cosmology emerged (or so Ginzburg argues) from an oral peasant tradition; and that he shot off his mouth on the subject for thirty years in the Friuli (the northernmost part of the Venetian provinces) without getting turned in, and when he *was* finally turned in, it was by a priest. Menocchio was thus very likely the tip of the iceberg, the bulk consisting of an ancient animistic tradition existing beneath the surface of a church-dominated society, and which the church had apparently failed to eradicate. The life of the shadows, then, becomes the real life of the Friuli—the psychic, social, and intellectual life all rolled into one. This is history from the inside, then; yet how are we to know that Ginzburg's guesswork is correct? After all, Menocchio could conceivably be an aberration, as some critics have contended.[18] Here, in a footnote, Ginzburg counters with an argument that might be seen as an evasion but that opens up the very possibility I am discussing. Arguing for the existence of a reciprocal relationship that obtains between written and oral culture, or between the visible and the hidden, Ginzburg says that it

> imposes on the historian standards of proof different from the usual. This is due to the fact that dominant culture and subordinate culture are matched in an unequal struggle, where the dice are loaded. Given the fact that the documentation reflects the relationship of power

between the classes of a given society, the possibility that the culture of the subordinate classes should leave a trace, even a distorted one, in a period in which illiteracy was so common, was indeed slim. At this point, to accept the usual standards of proof entails exaggerating the importance of the dominant culture. . . . [T]o assure that every scrap of written evidence . . . is of greater validity in the reconstruction of Menocchio's ideas than a "purely" oral tradition . . . means deciding the issue in advance in favor of one (the more privileged) of the contenders on the field. In this way we inevitably finish by "demonstrating" the traditional thesis that ideas by definition originate *always and only* in educated circles . . . in the heads of monks and university professors, certainly not of millers or of peasants. . . . [I]t would be advisable to develop new criteria of proof specifically suited to a line of research based on so thoroughly a heterogeneous, in fact unbalanced, documentation. That a new field of investigation alters not only the methods but the very criteria of proofs in a given discipline is shown, for example, in the history of physics: the acceptance of atomic theory has necessitated a change in the standards of evidence that had developed within the sphere of classical physics. [19]

The interesting thing, as many physicists have noted, is that quantum mechanics, in contrast with classical physics, recognizes no independent observer. The scientist is part of his or her own experiment; his or her very presence changes the course of the events. If modern historiography continues to evolve, and if it follows its own historical trend of imitating the methodology of contemporary physics, it could conceivably develop into a participative, or interactive, mode. It could understand that on the "subatomic" level, so to speak, there are no independent observers, and that experiential identification is dialectically the route to objective understanding.

Consider a single example. Some time ago I received a letter from a colleague informing me that he had just completed a history of anger. I have not yet read the manuscript, but I confess I was very excited by the possibility of such a book; a history of anger would have been inconceivable even ten years ago. But my basic reaction was this: There are two possible books that could be written on this subject. In one, my colleague simply obtains, from written documents, information on how anger functioned in the past and how its expression evolved over time. In the other, my colleague would do all of this and one thing more—he would spend a long time exploring his own anger, experiencing it, watching when and how it surfaced or was repressed, and observing the consequences of this expression or lack of it. It seems to me that the second book would be a very different one from the first; and although I cannot prove it, because the events are "subatomic," I submit that this work would be a lot closer to the historical truth than the first one.

There are dangers here, of course, the most obvious being that of projecting one's own anger onto historical situations that did not involve anger, or a particular mode of expressing anger, as part of their pattern. This remains a genuine pitfall and will need a lot of methodological discussion. My own belief about the validity of this approach is based on a dialectical premise as to how the body operates. Unlived or repressed emotions have different consequences from ones that are expressed. Having direct, personal experience of anger enables one to write a very different sort of history than one could write without having such experience. The difference is an *interior* experience—one of empathy and therefore of insight. But as noted, there is no way I can prove I am correct about this. At this point in the evolution of modern historiography, my suggestion of experiential identification remains only that, a suggestion; nevertheless, it is one that I think we ought to play around with. As the British historian Theodore Zeldin puts it, the "quality of a historian's personal experience is ultimately decisive in determining the quality of his writings." But it is more than that; and Zeldin adds that he looks forward to the day when "the historian who can discover the links between his own life and what has happened in past centuries, who can express in a new way how the past is alive, or who can give it a new colouring through the sieve of his own idiosyncrasies, will no longer be idiosyncratic."[20] I suspect that day will not be here for a while yet, but I am convinced it is coming nonetheless.

Undoubtedly, the issue of experiential identification will have to be worked out in specific ways and in particular historical contexts. A history of anger, in its entirety, for example, would be too cosmic to deal with between the covers of a single book. But before we go on to consider possible contexts, an obvious question presents itself: Why do this at all? Why concern ourselves with interior "microevents" of this sort? What difference does the history of anger, laughter, or play, or topics such as these make for the "real" events of history, the major historical dramas?

The popular comic strip by Lynn Johnston, "For Better or For Worse," put this question rather starkly on one occasion. Mother is sitting in front of the radio, listening to the news report; young daughter, home from school, is babbling to her about what happened in school that day ("And then Johnny took a frog out of his pocket, and . . ."). Finally, mother turns to daughter and says, "Elizabeth, be quiet! Can't you see I'm trying to listen to the news?" Elizabeth goes to her room, thinking: "I thought that's what I was *telling* you!"

What is "the news"? What are "real events"? How is it that the story of the plane hijacked in Costa Rica is news, but the one about Johnny and the frog is not? I am not making some sort of moral point here about how we should pay attention to our kids. My point is cognitive and analytical: What happens on an immediate, local, and experiential level is primary, and it finally determines macroevents such as wars and hijackings. We have been deluded as to what the "real dramas of history" are.

An analogy with the history of modern psychiatry might be helpful here. Until very recently, psychoanalysts assumed that neurotic behavior was the result of early traumatic events, and much therapeutic practice was preoccupied with helping the patient work through these traumas. After several decades of this approach, a number of therapists began to experiment with another possibility (although the trauma model, to be sure, can hardly be dismissed): The real neurotic scars are less the result of one-time traumatic shocks than of the daily habits of family life. Personality is generally a posture of defense, and one learns what one must defend oneself against in the context of what is regular, rather than what is aberrant.[21] In this later theory, the core of the adult personality is formed by what was, in the formative years, not traumatic but daily, repetitive, even boring. Like grain dropping upon grain, as one character in a Beckett play says, the whole structure is slowly built up, out of almost invisible microevents. And it is these that must be investigated if the larger structure is to be understood. What *sustains* laughter, play, anxiety, or anger? These are the icons of personality, and it is on this level that the riddle of personality has to be unraveled.

Historical studies, it seems to me, have to begin entertaining the notion that an analogous procedure is going on and that an analogous shift of focus will therefore have to take place. Historians typically study economic depressions, political revolutions, the impact of greater or lesser thinkers; they look at patterns of population, the distribution of wealth, the statistics of immigration, the occurrence of major or minor wars. Most of this falls into the "trauma" category, and as in the case of the psychoanalytic situation, it can hardly be called unreal. But the less visible may be, as I have suggested, more real, or at least more significant. Claude Charron, a former Québec politician, wrote of his disenchantment with politics because of its tendency to create a "deforming prism," by which one comes to believe that history consists of mass movements, broad categories of people, and large-scale events. According to this view, wrote Charron, people

are workers, they are the elderly, they are people on welfare, they are natives, they are people from the Gaspé, they are union members, they are people on the margins of society. No politics can be done without the abbreviation of differences, no government would know how to act without these indispensable categorizations; these categorizations make the newspapers live, and no one officially denies them.

. . . These clusters, we say, make history: we mention the Bastille, we point to insurrections.

But, he says, this mode of analysis is a duplicity, for these clusters are only heightened episodes that explode out of the real events of life, events that are hidden and subterranean and that remain imperceptible when we insist on viewing history from a great height. The truth, he concludes, is that

history is not made by parties, unions, groupings, demonstrations. It is discreetly woven in the souls and hearts, the successes, failures,

pains and joys of which are a thousand times nearer to the daily life of
each person.[22]

The challenge for history (that is, for historical analysis), as far as I
am concerned, is to start seeing the larger dramas in these somatic and
subatomic terms, and to come up with a methodology that convincingly relates the visible to the invisible.

Let me close this discussion with three examples that I think might
serve as possible models for generating a new kind of history. The first
is taken from a lecture I attended in 1983 by Brian Sutton-Smith,
professor of education at the University of Pennsylvania. His talk was
entitled "The Role of Toys in the Modern World."[23] He pointed out
that in the previous ten years (roughly 1972 to 1982) in the United
States, toys had become a six-billion-dollar industry; that 70 percent
of them were purchased for children by parents at Christmas, suggesting that they served a form of bonding function for the family at a
stressful time; but that their essential function was to induce separation or isolation, for most toys are designed to be played with by the
child in a solitary situation ("Go play by yourself," we typically say to
a youngster). Sutton-Smith also noted that a toy in this sense—a
device specifically designed for enabling solitary activity among
children—was only about two hundred years old. Before about 1750,
the historical pattern was *group* play, *group* toys. This phenomenon
thus constitutes a real historical break, a break with tribal culture and
custom. From 1750 on, the tendency has been to induce solitariness
in children, which really amounts to teaching them to tolerate loneliness by diverting themselves with objects and object relations. If we
want, then, to understand how modern Western culture managed to
inculcate values of individuality and achievement ("success"), how it
essentially managed to make people "happy" with isolation and object
relations instead of human relations, a history of toys might be an
important place to look. Sutton-Smith also noted that toys have been
fatal to street games, which have disappeared except among the lower
classes. The result, he said, is a fatality for the body, for the physical
self. The body is left behind by an entire generation mesmerized by
video games; and the consequences for a culture becoming disposed or

softened (conditioned) to certain larger, more "visible" possibilities are enormous. So the history of toys is really a history of the body; and my guess is that it can tell us quite a lot about the causes of what we customarily call "real" history—the stuff that makes it into the six o'clock news and the textbooks.

Yet to understand the psychic dimension revealed by toys, something more is needed here. Sutton-Smith, or whoever chooses to approach the modern isolated psyche and the cult of individualism in terms of toys, would need to endow the research with a special kind of quality by trying to relive mentally his or her own childhood experience with toys. This need not necessarily be part of the final published work on the history of toys (though it might); the point is that the investigator must enter into the experiment, to break down the methodological principle of psychic distance. What will result, I cannot say; but to sit for several weeks playing with the wooden toys of our youth, as well as with the plastic toys of today's youth—to feel the difference physically, in one's hands—is (I suspect) to open the door to a very different sort of historical understanding. To some extent, a history of the body reflected in the evolution of toys has to be a history of the author's body as he or she experienced them. How exciting it would be to read a history textbook or monograph that resonated with this kind of energy.

A second example of embodied history occurred to me after I ran across a quotation from a German child-rearing manual published in 1787 and reproduced in Alice Miller's book *For Your Own Good*. The author, J. Oest, points out the need for sex education among children but adds that such information will typically inflame the childhood imagination. Children, he says, should be given a knowledge of what the genitals of the opposite sex look like; but how to do this safely? Pictures are far too provocative, he maintains. Oest's solution is as follows:

> All these worries disappear if one makes use of a lifeless human body for this purpose. The sight of a corpse evokes solemnity and reflection, and this is the most appropriate mood for a child under such circumstances. By a natural association of ideas, his memory of the scene will

> also produce a solemn frame of mind in the future . . . [E]very teacher
> can . . . impart the necessary instruction in [this] manner. . . . There
> is often opportunity to see a corpse.[24]

Now suppose this manner of sex education actually took hold after
1787 and lasted through the nineteenth century and into the twentieth. (I have no idea whether this was the case or not.) Suppose,
through an investigation of other child-rearing manuals, or interviews
with German and Austrian octogenarians, or school records of field
trips to morgues, we could establish that historically, this mode of
instruction was widespread. I would suggest that such an investigation would tell us infinitely more about the Third Reich and the
Holocaust than any number of psychobiographies of Hitler, no matter
how valuable. That Hitler was psychotic, that women had to defecate
on him in order for him to be able to make love, is all very titillating,
but it tells us nothing about why such an individual managed to
pluck a responsive chord in an entire population. Hitler's appeal
would be a lot more understandable if it turned out that a number of
generations prior to 1933 had a sexual education in childhood that
taught them to associate sex with death. This is history of the body of
a more profound and convincing sort. One might also wonder, if
Oest's book had a wide following in Austria, whether Freud's theory of
the death instinct, and of civilization as a war between Eros and
Thanatos, did not have its roots in the clinical results of such upbringing among adults. The death instinct always struck me as the weakest
stone in the Freudian edifice, but it would not seem so strange an
invention if the entire culture in which Freud lived had been trained
to associate sex with death on an unconscious level. In this way, too,
such a study would enable us to make better sense of the intellectual
history of that period.

Once again, there is a further subjective step to be taken here. How
does the investigator feel about his or her own sexuality? Granted, the
facts of life may not have been learned in a morgue (although,
interestingly enough, generations of American medical students had
their first exposure to the subject in autopsy rooms); but how pre-

cisely does the historian's own psyche differ from the German one? What do his or her dreams reveal about this? What are the investigator's specific fears regarding sexual behavior and expression? How about making a trip to the morgue today? What sorts of reactions does he or she have to the genitals of a corpse? Again, there is a lot that has to be worked out here methodologically; one reason that I am groping in the dark is that we do not *have* methodologies of feeling, only methodologies of analysis. But a start has to be made.

My final example is a remarkable book by Norbert Elias called *The History of Manners,* a book that falls into the *mentalité* category and was first published (in German) in 1939. Elias was able to chart the emergence of a phenomenon he called the "advancing threshold of shame" in the transition from medieval to modern Europe. He took as his subject the daily, repetitive habits of table manners, including nose blowing, farting, the use of utensils, burping, and so on. From the point of view of almost any school of historiography, it is a most bizarre book. Yet the exploration of the daily details of etiquette enabled him to show that the major form of control that emerged in modern society was a form of social distancing—not unrelated to modern scientific or historical methodology, as it turns out—whereby people modify their behavior on the basis of how they see themselves being perceived by those around them. This "mirroring" phenomenon began to have its echoes in the etiquette books of the time, such as *De civilitate morum puerilium* (On Civility in Boys, 1530), by Erasmus of Rotterdam. Thus Erasmus wrote: "Some people put their hands in the dishes the moment they have sat down. Wolves do that. . . ."[25] Other texts, especially after 1600, reveal a preoccupation with how one will appear to an observer—a preoccupation that requires taking a position regarding oneself as a "specimen," an object of contemplation. Very slowly, said Elias, the modern European upper and middle classes came to observe their behavior in a detached, self-conscious manner, one that contrasted sharply with the spontaneity and "blurriness" of the behavior of the Middle Ages.

So far so good; and as a history of the body, and of mind-body relationships, the book has much to commend it. But to his credit,

Elias did not stop there; he extrapolated from this minute, daily behavior to a major cultural shift, namely the Scientific Revolution itself:

> The development of the idea that the earth circles round the sun in a purely mechanical way in accordance with natural laws—that is, in a way not in the least determined by any purpose relating to mankind, and therefore no longer possessing any great emotional significance for men—presupposed and demanded at the same time a development in human beings themselves toward increased emotional control, a greater restraint of their spontaneous feeling that everything they experience and everything that concerns them takes its stamp from them. . . .
>
> Herein lies one of the keys to the question of why the problem of scientific knowledge took on the form of classical European epistemology familiar today. The detachment of the thinking subject from his objects in the act of cognitive thought, and the affective restraint that is demanded, did not appear to those thinking about it at this stage as an act of distancing but as a distance actually present, as an eternal condition of spatial separation between a mental apparatus apparently locked "inside" man, an "understanding" or "reason," and the objects "outside" and divided from it by an invisible wall.[26]

The implications of such a suggestion are enormous. The rise of modern science has been studied from the vantage point of the history of ideas, or in terms of concomitant social and economic factors; and there is no doubt that both of these approaches have been fruitful. But it has never been studied as a *bodily* phenomenon, and surely Elias— whose suggestion was never picked up—was on to something very important. What he grasped was the subatomic stratum, the possibility that the educated classes of Western Europe learned the phenomenon of detachment and observation *in their bodies* for two centuries preceding Newton, and that a Newton (or a Copernicus, or a Galileo) could not have arisen or been comprehensible in a culture that had not had such a visceral apprenticeship. In a like manner, the success of the heliocentric theory, or of atomism, required of people a radical distrust of sensory evidence (it still does), a kind of detachment that was simply not part of the medieval European psyche, probably for reasons discussed by Elias. In this regard, it is interesting that to this day, the modern scientific paradigm has made the least headway among those cultures whose table manners, from our point of view, are the sloppiest.

What else might Elias have done? I think back to a course I once took in sixteenth-century Italian court dance. As background, we began the first class with medieval dance. The movements were light, and the dances were all done in group formation, similar in style to the Virginia reel; there was no partner dancing. We then switched to the dances of the late Renaissance, and the difference in physical sensation was immediate and dramatic; one felt it most clearly in the pelvis. The sensation was: "This is *my* space I am standing on, *my* property." The sense of deliberateness, aggressiveness, and privatization (individuality) was unmistakable, and I would never have experienced it merely from reading about the history of dance. Have I been deceived? Possibly; but possibly also, I understand something about the physicality of modernity that I would otherwise have missed.

In the same way, Elias pointed out that, as we can see in numerous paintings, medieval people struck postures that seem very strange to us—for example, standing on one leg for long periods of time. (There are tribes in various parts of Africa that still do this.) Why not suggest that the reader go and do this, before reading any further? Why should Elias not, as a historian, do this himself? Or to take another example, he charted the evolution of the spoon, from the large round soup spoon that was virtually the only spoon in the Middle Ages, to the tapered teaspoon more shaped to the mouth that is used today (this evolution can be seen at the Victoria and Albert Museum in London). Why is this significant? Because as part of the history of manners, the large spoon was sloppier, much less efficient; it reflected the spontaneity of eating during the Middle Ages, whereas the tapered spoon reflects the self-conscious eating and etiquette of the modern period. To understand that spontaneity, to really feel it in your body, you would have to eat with a large spoon for several weeks, feeling how it stretched your mouth, at first uncomfortably, until finally the sensation of throwing the mouth wide open—the grimace of the medieval gargoyle—seemed perfectly natural. Perhaps Elias could have instructed his publisher to attach such a spoon to every copy of the book, with instructions to the reader to eat all meals with it for the next few weeks (having first, presumably, done so himself).

It is easy to dismiss all of this as sheer idiocy, but I am not so sure. Recent research in neuropsychology has tended to confirm the notion that personality changes in individuals precipitate serious alterations in their bodies. It seems likely to me that the reverse is also true—that bodily changes or conditioning would create serious alterations in personality—and, moreover, that the "personality," and therefore the history, of an entire culture could undergo profound shifts in orientation as well. Toys, sex education, and eating habits are all good examples of slow, cumulative body training that can finally make a profound difference in the definition of reality itself. What Elias had to say about scientific detachment, for example, could equally apply to the emergence of perspective in art, to which I have already alluded, in which the convergence of lines to an infinite distance or vanishing point puts the viewer in the position of a neutral observer, standing at an ideal spot outside of the painting. And it could apply as well to modern historical analysis, where the historian arranges a linear chronology of events of a particular kind—namely, those experienced in a detached fashion—and where subjective experience of them is seen to violate the canons of the discipline itself. If Elias's book seems bizarre to most historians, and my extrapolation of it idiotic, perhaps we ought to reflect, once again, upon where our standards of the "reasonable" and "sensible" come from. For they are rooted in a commitment to psychic distancing and somatic nonengagement; and we learn that commitment physically, as young children. What took Europe several hundred years to assimilate in terms of table manners has been compressed into the first five or six years of life for those of us born in the twentieth century. The historian who finds these suggestions ridiculous may only be acting out, on an "adult" and "mature" intellectual level, the effects of that early visceral apprenticeship. There may be more than one way to look at all this.

━━━

The issue of visceral apprenticeship, then, is something that we must start to apply to ourselves in the investigation of historical or cultural phenomena; only then will the criteria of historical proof start to change. *Mentalité* is fine, an immense advance over what came before and over what still remains the historical mainstream. But as Carlo Ginzburg notes, we are finally up against the methodological edge of the old paradigm, and in my view we need to take a leap to what we might call *corporéalité,* a visceral approach to history that puts the mind and body back together again. Once again, I have to say that this is not necessarily a reversion to storytelling or to archaic modes of understanding; the goal should be a post-Cartesian paradigm, not a pre-Cartesian one. But this new methodology would involve our bodies as well as our minds; it would create bodily and emotional echoes in the person who reads historical studies reconstructed on its basis. It would elaborate on a suggestion made many years ago by the Austrian psychiatrist Wilhelm Reich, that the way we hold our bodies—what he called the "character structure"—"is the congealed sociological process of a given epoch,"[27] and that as a result, our bodies might be the key to the historical dramas we seek to understand. Above all, *corporéalité* would link the visible with the invisible, put the macrocosm back together with the microcosm.

We are in murky territory here, in the same way that the physicists are; no physicist I know of has managed to construct a methodology that directly involves the experimeter in the experiment. But that day may not be far off. Our history has been disembodied long enough; the time has come to flesh it out.

NOTES

[1] Edmund Leach, "Common Ground," *London Review of Books,* September 19, 1985, p. 19.

[2] Ibid.

[3] Eric Havelock, *Preface to Plato* (Cambridge: Harvard University Press, 1963), pp. 25–27, pp. 45–47, and pp. 150–158.

280 *Morris Berman*

4 Thomas Goldstein, *Dawn of Modern Science* (Boston: Houghton Mifflin, 1980), pp. 156–166.

5 Kurt Goldstein, *Selected Papers/Ausgewählte Schriften,* ed. Aron Gurwitsch *et al.* (The Hague: Martinus Nijhoff, 1971), p. 430.

6 Of course, many historians, such as E. H. Carr, claim that objectivity is not strictly possible and that the historian's bias inevitably colors the picture, but in the end, Carr, like so many others, remains a positivist; he finally does believe in a "hard bedrock of reality" that can be contacted via the documents. See E. H. Carr, *What Is History?* (Harmondsworth, Middlesex: Penguin, 1964).

7 Lewis Mumford, *The Myth of the Machine* (New York: Harcourt, Brace and World, 1966), pp. 3–24; see also pp. 48–71.

8 Charles Darwin, *On the Origin of Species, A Facsimile of the First Edition* (Cambridge: Harvard University Press, 1964), p. 288.

9 On the following, see R. D. Laing, *The Divided Self* (Harmondsworth, Middlesex: Penguin, 1965), p. 25 and pp. 86–87.

10 See Andrei Bely, *Petersburg,* trans. Robert A. Maguire and John E. Malmstad (Bloomington: Indiana University Press, 1978; orig. Russian ed. 1916), pp. 162–168.

11 Elsa Morante, *History, A Novel,* trans. William Weaver (New York: Vintage Books, 1984), pp. 200–215 and pp. 287–292.

12 There is a good bit of work by, and about, the *Annales* school, whose most famous representative is undoubtedly the late Fernand Braudel. A major study of the school can be found in Traian Stoianovich, *French Historical Method: The Annales Paradigm* (Ithaca, NY: Cornell University Press, 1976). In addition, the interested reader might wish to consult the school's journal, *Annales. Economies, Sociétés, Civilisations.*

13 Lucien Febvre, *The Problem of Unbelief in the Sixteenth Century,* trans. Beatrice Gottlieb (Cambridge: Harvard University Press, 1983; orig. French ed. 1947); Marc Bloch, *The Royal Touch,* trans. J. E. Anderson (London: Routledge and Kegan Paul, 1973; orig. French ed. 1924).

14 There are a number of discussions of work done in *mentalité* the reader may wish to consult: Stuart Clark, "French Historians and Early Modern Popular Culture," *Past and Present,* 100 (1983), pp. 62–99; Philippe Ariès, "L'histoire des mentalités," in Jacques Le Goff *et al.* (eds.), *La Nouvelle histoire* (Paris: Retz, 1978), pp. 402–423; André Burguière, "The

Fate of the History of Mentalities in the *Annales," Comparative Studies in Society and History*, 24, 3 (1982), pp. 424–437; and other essays by Patrick Hutton, Jacques Le Goff, Alphonse Dupront, Georges Duby, and Robert Mandrou.

15 Foucault's works include *Madness and Civilization, The Birth of the Clinic, Discipline and Punish, The History of Sexuality, The Order of Things*, and *The Archaeology of Knowledge*, and numerous studies of his works are now available in both French and English. Ariès is the author of *Centuries of Childhood* and *The Hour of Our Death*, among other works; a discussion of his contribution to historiography may be found in André Burguière, "La singulière histoire de Philippe Ariès," *Le Nouvel observateur*, February 20, 1978, pp. 80–101.

16 Michel Foucault, *The Order of Things* (New York: Vintage Books, 1973), esp. ch. 2; Patrick H. Hutton, "The History of Mentalities: The New Map of Cultural History," *History and Theory*, 20 (1981), p. 252.

17 G. Spencer-Brown, *Laws of Form* (New York: E. P. Dutton, 1979), esp. p. xxix and pp. 105–106.

18 For example, Paola Zambelli, "Uno, due, tre, mille Menocchio?" *Archivio storico italiano*, 137 (1979), pp. 51–90.

19 Carlo Ginzburg, *The Cheese and the Worms*, trans. John and Anne Tedeschi (New York: Penguin, 1982), p. 155.

20 Theodore Zeldin, "Personal History and the History of the Emotions," *Journal of Social History*, 15 (Spring 1982), pp. 339–347.

21 See, for example, John Bradshaw, *Bradshaw On: The Family* (Deerfield Beach, Fla.: Health Communications, 1988).

22 Claude Charron, *Désobéir* (Montreal: VLB Éditeur, 1983), pp. 346–347.

23 This talk was given at the University of Victoria (British Columbia) on September 28, 1983. Sutton-Smith is the author of roughly a dozen books on education, child psychology, games, and play. Most relevant to the topic being discussed here is *Toys as Culture* (New York: Gardner Press, 1986).

24 Quoted in Alice Miller, *For Your Own Good*, trans. Hildegarde and Hunter Hannum (New York: Farrar, Straus and Giroux, 1983), p. 46.

25 Quoted in Norbert Elias, *The History of Manners*, trans. Edmund Jephcott (New York: Pantheon, 1978), p. 89.

26 Ibid., p. 256.

27 Wilhelm Reich, *Character Analysis*, trans. Vincent R. Carfagno, 3rd ed., enl. (New York: Simon & Schuster, 1972; orig. German ed. 1933), p. xxvi (italicized in the original).

Contributors

Mary Catherine Bateson is Robinson Professor of Anthropology and English, George Mason University, and author of *With a Daughter's Eye: A Memoir of Margaret Mead and Gregory Bateson* (Morrow/Pocket Books); *Composing a Life* (Atlantic Monthly Press); with Gregory Bateson, *Angel's Fear: Toward an Epistemology of the Sacred* (Macmillan/Bantam); and with Richard A. Goldsby, *Thinking AIDS* (Addison Wesley). *Sevanne Margaret Kassarjian* is a student at Brown University.

Morris Berman is an author, lecturer, and social critic. His published works include *Social Change and Scientific Organization* (Cornell University Press), and *The Reenchantment of the World* (Bantam). His essay in this issue is adapted from *Coming to Our Senses* (Simon and Schuster).

Doyne Farmer has worked on the theory of Chaos and nonlinear dynamical systems. In a previous incarnation, he proved that it was possible to beat roulette with a computer he wore in his shoe. Doyne is currently the head of the Complex Systems Group of the Theoretical Division at Los Alamos National Laboratory, where he is working on Artificial Life, nonlinear time-series prediction, and machine learning.

Gerald Feinberg, a particle physicist, is a professor of physics at Columbia University, and author of *Life Beyond Earth* (with Robert Shapiro, William Morrow) and *Solid Clues* (Simon & Schuster).

Howard Gardner is a psychologist and director of Project Zero at the Harvard University School of Education. He is the author of *Frames of Mind: The Theory of Multiple Intelligences* (Basic), *The Mind's New Science: A History of the Cognitive Revolution* (Basic), and *To Open Minds* (Basic).

Chris Langton is a computer scientist in the Complex Systems Group of the Theoretical Division at Los Alamos National Laboratory, where he organized the first workshop on Artificial Life in 1987. His current research interests include Artificial Life, the physics of computation, fine-grained parallelism, and scientific visualization.

Joshua Meyrowitz, professor of communication at the University of New Hampshire, is the author of *No Sense of Place: The Impact of Electronic Media on Social Behavior* (Oxford University Press).

Mark Jay Mirsky, novelist, is professor of English, City College of New York and the editor of *Fiction* magazine. He is the author of *Blue Hill Avenue* and *Thou Worm Jacob*.

Joan Richardson is a biographer, professor of English at City University of New York, and author of *Wallace Stevens: The Early Years 1879–1923* (Morrow), and *Wallace Stevens: The Later Years 1923–1955* (Morrow).

Paul Ryan, cyberneticist and video artist, is the author of *Cybernetics of the Sacred*. His video work has been shown at the Museum of Modern Art and the Cathedral of St. John the Divine.

Roger Schank, professor of psychology and computer science, Yale University, is author of *The Cognitive Computer* (with Peter Childers, Addison Wesley), and *The Creative Attitude: Learning To Ask and Answer the Right Questions* (Scribners).

Vitaly Shevoroshkin, linguist, is professor of slavic languages and literatures at the University of Michigan.

John Woodford, journalist, is executive editor of the University of Michigan publication, *Michigan Today*.

About the Editor

JOHN BROCKMAN, founder of The Reality Club and editor of The Reality Club series of books, is a writer and literary agent. He is the author of *By The Late John Brockman* (Macmillan, 1969), *37* (Holt Rinehart Winston, 1970), *Afterwords* (Anchor, 1973), and *The Philosopher's Game* (with Edwin Schlossberg; St. Martins, 1975), and editor of *About Bateson* (Dutton, 1977).